The Dubbalin Man

The Dubbalin Man

Brendan Behan

A new selection from his
Irish Press articles 1954–6,
with a previously unpublished story
'Christmas Eve in the graveyard'
and decorations by Beatrice Behan
and a foreword by Anthony Cronin

© Text and drawings Estate of Brendan Behan 1954–6, 1963, 1997
© Foreword Anthony Cronin 1997
© Selection and notes A. & A. Farmar 1997

British Library Cataloguing in Publication Data
A CIP catalogue record for this book is available from the British
Library

Typesetting by A. & A. Farmar
Cover design by Jacques Teljeur
Printed and bound by Betaprint

A. & A. Farmar
Beech House
78 Ranelagh Village
Dublin 6
Ireland

ISBN 1 899047 15 8

Contents

[v   ]

Foreword

by Anthony Cronin

These pieces here gathered are the nearest simulacrum of Brendan Behan talking that we have, except for a few fragmentary tape-recordings. Those who knew him will immediately recognise the style and the tone, and much of the content will be familiar to them too.

He scatters good jokes around with the utmost prodigality. There are several in the very first piece, including the memorable: 'I am one of the compulsory Irish'. He often loses the point of his discourse, but makes several other points of a perhaps more valuable nature while he is about it. And he rejoices in the fact that he is a living repository of Dublin speech and folk lore.

A lot of his jokes are music-hall, but they are first-class music-hall. The old gentleman asks the lady in the bookshop if she has a copy of the New Testament. 'Desperate sorry I am, sir,' she says, 'but I'm afraid it's not out yet. We have the old one, of course, but I suppose you've read that.'

There is an extraordinary mélange of cultures and cultural cross-references here. Not only is Dublin a cultural entity, separate from the 'three other provinces, Cork, the North and the Country' and rather distrustful of them, but the various parts of Dublin, north side, south side, are distinguished from each other by different social and cultural traditions and characteristics ('The Coombe crowd are hot stuff'). Those who remember the Dublin of those days will recollect that they were distinguished from each other in just this way in the material that Harry O'Donovan, another Dublin-born former apprentice house-painter, wrote over the years of Brendan's lifetime for his friend and fellow-Dubliner, the great comedian Jimmy O'Dea.

Brendan is quite encyclopaedic about Dublin, its geography and its local history, as he is about many other things. But he usually saves himself from any suspicion of pedantry by turning his arcane knowledge into a joke. He notes, for example, that there is no song about the Tolka river, once a great north-side institution, but, 'as the man said, if it wasn't much of a river, it was the best we had.' And furthermore, 'Brian Boru's son was drowned in it, and it's not every river you could say that about.'

But he is by no means provincial. Both France and England are very much part of his cultural grid. The affection he has for ordinary English people is evident, as is his knowledge of their principal preoccupations, chief among them royalty and murder. Some of this knowledge is special to him, as are such matters as the geography of Paris or Gertrude Stein's last words. But some of it is part of his Dublin upbringing: the Dublin working class was particularly close to England, then as now, nationalist though it might also be. Queen Victoria was an oddly important figure in Dublin's consciousness when Brendan was growing up, as were the names of the Irish regiments of the British Army, particularly the Dublin Fusiliers, and the campaigns they fought, down to and including the First World War. This side of Ireland's past is as familiar to him and almost as much a part of his rearing and general background as is 1916.

All of these pieces with one exception belong to the contributions he made to the *Irish Press* in the mid–1950s. This was the period just before the success of *The Quare Fellow* in Joan Littlewood's production at Stratford East in London brought him success and celebrity. They are, of course, to some extent modelled on Myles na Gopaleen's contributions to the *Irish Times*—which in turn derive to some extent from 'Beachcomber', J. B. Morton of the *Daily Express*, who invented the comic newspaper column with its own cast of characters and running themes—another example of English–Irish cultural pollination.

Given the nature of Brendan's relationship with some Dublin groupings of that time, however, they are surprisingly unsatirical; and he never manifests Myles's occasional fierceness, nor imitates his snarl. The targets, if there can be said to be targets, are generalised and blurred. Satire is not the aim and I, at least, do not recognise any individuals or cliques here. What we have, though, is unmistakably Dublin, a goldmine for social historians, a paradise for linguists and lexicographers, and a great pleasure for readers who want to recapture some of the flavour of a past that, though recent enough, is in the process of vanishing.

The exception among these pieces is 'Christmas Eve in the graveyard', a short story probably written some time in the early fifties. This introduces some of the characters later to be found, with dream-like transformations, in the column—Maria Concepta, Denis the Bookie—and some of the background themes, too,—the Dublin Fusilier who came back, as so many others did not, from the Dardanelles, his son who died during the Normandy landings. Underneath the emphasis on the picturesque, and the flippant tone of the narration is a very real pathos and an accurate depiction of what Dublin city life was really like. The fusilier, separated from his wife, had a fancy-woman, who turns up at the funeral. There is an undertone of harsh realism here, a vein one wishes he had explored more often, or at least more steadily. But the *Irish Press* columns have their own authenticity and it is good to see them now back in print.

Anthony Cronin
December 1997

Publishers' preface

Brendan Behan's articles began to appear in the *Irish Press* in March 1954 and continued in an almost unbroken series until April 1956. They appeared every Saturday, on the leader page in the centre of the newspaper. His previous most extended piece of journalism had been the thirty episodes of *The Scarperer*, which he published in *The Irish Times* from 19 October 1953 under the pseudonym of Emmet Street. Just under a hundred articles appeared in the *Irish Press*, and the series came to an end just before *The Quare Fellow* opened in the Theatre Royal, Stratford, in May 1956.

The articles were widely read at the time for their humour and for Brendan's superb ear for dialogue. About a quarter of the articles re-produced here have never been re-published; 'Christmas Eve in the Graveyard' has never been published before.

A previous selection of these articles was published by Hutchinson at the height of Brendan's fame in 1963 under the title *Hold Your Hour and Have Another*. By way of easing the English reader into the book, the selection began with 'A seat on the Throne' in which an Irish house-painter meets the Queen. This was in fact originally pub-lished towards the end of the series, in February 1956.

We have restored the articles to the original order of their writing, which has the advantage of reviving narrative links that had been lost, and we have also restored their original long titles. For instance, the story published as 'Let's go to town' was originally, and more interest-ingly, titled 'Let's go to town, and hear what they have to say about us'. In all but two cases, the text has been checked against the original in the *Irish Press*.

The articles contain a wide range of national and literary folklore, of Dublin sayings, local jokes and references to Irish history. Although these sketches were written by an avowed republican in the 1950s, a notably introverted period, the British Army bulks large, reflecting the real experience of the Dublin working-class. Brendan's characters take part in the Boer War and the First World War, fight on both sides of the War of Independence, spend time in pubs and in prisons. As in the best Dublin stories, there is exaggeration and fantasy, as well as a disdain for excessive precision. It is up to the reader to make sense of what is being said.

Brendan is just as vivid in describing the trouble the family had with a mule that slept the night in 1924 (when he was one year old) as in his enthusiasm for de Valera's election victory in 1932 (when he was nine). The veterans' tales cannot be taken as gospel, either. In one story, 'The Hot Malt Man and the Bores', Kinsella boasts of the number of 'bores' he killed in the siege of Bloemfontein, and how General Roberts recognised him from the time they had served together in Egypt. As it happens, Bloemfontein was abandoned by the Boers without a fight, and Roberts, unlike Kitchener, never served in Egypt. The glossary provides a background to these references, though we have been conscious that a joke explained is a joke killed.

The publishers would like to acknowledge the help of Padraic Hanratty, Harry Boylan and Peter Costello in the compilation of the glossary. We would further like to thank Liam O'Leary and John de Vere White for access to the typescript of 'Christmas Eve in the Graveyard' and Tom Nesbitt's painting, and Brian Fallon whose article in *The Irish Times* originally alerted us to their existence.

Spring—it brings back memories of Dublin, London and Paris in the hopeful days of May

How am I? If I was any better I couldn't stick it. Farewell to foul winter, spring has come at last, nothing I have gained, but my true love I have lost. As regards that part of the transaction, it's a question of who was losing who. As Joyce says, one story is good till you hear another. But honest, that bit of sun the last few weeks was the making of us.

Seán Ó Faoláin tells us that Señor de Madariaga tells him that we are a Mediterranean people gone astray and lost up here in the damp cold of the far north. As they say on the waterfront of this newspaper, *Quien Sabe?*

Brian Merriman had it weighed up, in that front bit of 'The Midnight Court' we learned at school:

> *Ba ghnáth mé ag siúl, le chumhais na habhann,*
> *Ar mháinseach úr is an drúcht go trom . . .*

Considering my nationality (I am one of the compulsory Irish), I am quite fluent and almost comprehensible in the second official language.

(Proceeds to demonstrate this modest accomplishment):

> *'Twas my joy to walk the morning stream,*
> *The meadows fresh with the dew's wet gleam,*
> *Beside the woods, in the high hill's shade . . .*

In this city, in the old Georgian heart of the north side, now reconditioned flats for the use of the people whose ancestors built it, and in the new breathing spaces of the Dublin people—Cabra, Crumlin, Kimmage and Ballyfermot—are young men of twenty-one and twenty-two, enjoying the May weather and rejoicing, if that's what they call it, in the Christian name of 'Lauri'.

If they want to know, it's my mother's fault. Their mothers weren't strong-minded enough for her, the year of the Congress, when her edict went up and down the lower depth of the North Circular Road, that all male children, 1932 model, were to receive in baptism, the

[1]

name of the Papal Legate.

A decade or so earlier, in spite of some people she didn't like by the name of Murphy, and a local publican by the name of Byrne, they got 'Larkin' for a monicker.

Both lots hide under the diminutive of 'Larry' like any of the thousands named after the great O'Toole, but they'll be found out when they go looking for their voting papers.

If they want to make anything of it, they'll have to wait till she gets back from London, where she and my father have been assisting at the inauguration of my new niece.

This niece's mother was born the year of the Congress, is married a few years now and lives happily with her Scots husband and a previous daughter in Kensington, near, according to her direction or his, the Oval or the gasworks.

It makes me feel as bould as tay, to think that I took part in the election weeks before she was born, and sang and danced at the bonfire in the middle of NCR the night of the final result.

All over our side the whole night through, the flames leapt high, and the tri-colour topping the lamp-post, while we rent the winter air and the ears of the very respectable class of people lying sleepless, with songs and cheers for the Republic.

The fire brigade called to the bonfire in Gloucester Diamond, under the impression that the Custom House had moved up town and gone ablaze again.

And our own bonfire, construction supervised by 'Chuckles' Malone, head buck-cat round our corner, occupied, like the Bastille in the Place de Nation, the space at the junction of Emmet Street, Fitzgibbon Street, Russell Street and the North Circular Road, and could be seen from Summerhill to the Park Gate.

My mother was welcomed in London by a genial landlord, to whose hostelry she had been brought before by her connections, a redoubtable clique, drawn from the best society of Yorkshire, Glasgow and Dublin North-East.

To mark the occasion, this versatile man delivered his greetings in a jovially affected Irish accent.

'An' Mrs Bey Hann, and sure, and begorra, and how's the Ould Sod?'

'He'll be here in a minute,' said my mother, 'he came over with me, this time.'

'And how do you like London, this trip?'

'I always like it.'

'Brendan wouldn't stay five minutes in it,' said Jock, my brother-in-law.

'He wouldn't be let,' said my mother. 'They've too much sense. I like London, and I'd like to see Paris, too, before I die.'

'Not much chance of seeing it afterwards,' growled my other respected parent, who had arrived and was watching with a stern eye the man filling the local equivalent of a half. 'I hope you can spare all that.'

'Oh, certainly,' smiled mine host, politely.

'Wouldn't like to deprive sick people. Useful in an emergency.' Looking down into his glass. 'Is your thermometer broke or anything?'

And if my mother wants to see Paris, it had better be before she dies; it's only good Americans go there afterwards.

Myself and Jack Brennan sat outside the Mabillon, one fine May day with some of them. 'That's right,' said Brennan, who has lived in Paris, by various ways and means, since he was about twenty, as he says in charming candour about himself.

'It was either Paree or Glencree—we're Irish.'

'Say, I'm Irish too,' said this American, 'and so's my buddy, Herman, here.'

'Well,' said Herman, modestly, 'I'm really only half Irish.'

'I see,' said Brennan, looking at him as if to see which half.

'I'm from Boston,' said Herman's buddy, 'what part of the States are you from? New York, Philly, Chi?'

'We're not from the States, we're Irish we said,' said Brennan. 'We're from Dublin.'

'You're from Dublin, Ireland.'

'That's it. See, look at our passports.'

'Well, whaddyouknow. These guys, Herman, they're Irishmen, from

Ireland. I wondered they spoke so funny. Not like real Irishmen back home. And look here, this thing's got de Valera's autograph on it. Gee, how much do you want for this, buddy? I'll give you ten bucks. That's nearly four thousand francs.'

No man in the quarter knew the value of such an article better than Brennan. He let out a scream of fright, and dived to its rescue, and caught it to his bosom muttering incoherently:

'Votre papier, m'sieu? Liberté, egalité, carte d'identité.'

'Well, I only thought you might,' said Herman's buddy, sulkily. 'It looked real cute, with harp and green cover and all. Where would I get one? Can you get them in Paris?'

'Certainly,' said Brennan, '37 Rue Paul Valéry, off the Avenue Victor Hugo. Where it says Ambassade d'Irlande. You'll see one of these harps over the gate. You just go right in and ask.'

He smiled, cynical and heartless: 'Say Brendan Behan sent you.'

Irish Press 8 May 1954

Let's go to town and hear what they have to say about us

If you don't get up and get down town you'd hear nothing, nor find out what they're saying about you. And God send, they're saying something. Good or bad, it's better to be criticised than ignored.

And it was such a fine mild morning that even I was tempted out in the air. From the highlands of Kimmage you could see the mists rising off the city, and the sky rosy and pink out over the head of Howth. The time was seven o'clock, and if Roger Bannister could manage the mile in four minutes, I could get from Sundrive Road to a stationer's in Dame Street in two and a half hours.

I could and did, and had time over for a word with a friend outside the Irish House, at the bottom of Michael's Hill or Winetavern Street. Have it your own way.

Dressed in his sober black, and carrying a small black box, he rubbed his white moustache in greeting.

'You must have had a bad way of lying. It's not eight o'clock yet.'

'I rambled down from the house. I thought the walk would do me good. It's what you'd call close, though I'm sweating.'

'I'm going to wash off a ceiling for an old one in Foxrock. "Lot of dirt in this room, painter," she says to me yesterday. "I didn't bring any of it with me, ma'am," says I.'

'I've a second stock out with me. I don't suppose you'd care to come out and give us a hand?'

I shuddered. I'm allergic to stockbrushes and afraid of knives. Putty knives, hacking knives, and glazing knives.

'Well, I only asked. And you're sweating.'

I wiped my brow.

'You should save that, Brendan. There'd be a cure in that.'

'It's a bit early to be getting the Foxrock people out of bed. What about moseying over as far as the market and see how the fish and fruit and all to that effect are going on?'

'I suppose we might do worse. I could do with a rossiner myself.'

In Michael's they were listening to the radio, and only took their attention from it to greet us.

There was Mrs Brennan, and she and I know all belonging to each other from the time of the Invincibles, though her way of talking is infectious and I keep calling her 'Mrs Brenning'.

She comes down to deal and get her stuff out and on the road, as she's done this sixty years; though nowadays she directs operations from a seat in the corner, and children and grandchildren keep running in and out to get her directions on the price of this and who's to take what go-car of fish, fruit, or vegetables, where.

And Crippen, who has resigned from active participation in the great world of commerce and industry, and is by way of being a literary man to the extent of writing three cross-doubles for the female clientele of the bookies up the street. He also had a connection with a well-known literary journal, as a broker in International Reply Coupons, which he changed in the bookies.

'So your man is in London, eh?'

'A shocking lot in Londing,' says Mrs Brennan to her friend beside her, in the corner.

'Ah,' says Crippen, casually, 'it's an editor we used to know.'

'An editor,' murmurs Mrs Brennan to her friend, impressively. 'Mind that, now. If Mr Cripping and Mr Behing didn't go to school, they met the scholars coming back. It's all the educayshing.'

'Well,' smiled Crippen, modestly. 'I dare swear I could make out the odds to a hundred-to-eight shot as good as the next.

''Course this man was a Varsity man. National and Trinity and all to that effect.'

'Look at that now, Maria. In the Natural Trimity College.'

'He's on the Third Programme now,' said I.

'And the same fellow,' said Crippen. 'He could be on the First if he only minded himself.'

'And where do you leave Brending Behing, there, beside you? Took second prize of ten shillings or six pound of fresh beef at the Carnival in Mountjoy Square. Saw him myself. Not today nor yesterday. Playing the mouth-orging.'

She looked at my friend, the painter.

'It was in aid of the new hall in Phibsboro. Near Dalymount.'

'I know it up there,' said the painter. 'I worked in a presbytery not far from it. Grained and varnished the priests' desks.'

'Look at that now, Maria, what the man did. Varnished the priests' destes. You'll have luck with it, sir.'

'And I should be on my way out to a bit this morning.'

'Ah, hold your hour and have another. You should take Brending with you and get his weight down. I heard he gets his clothes made in the Hammongd Laying Fouingdry these times.

'Just wait till you hear a bit of this on the wireless. It's shocking funny.'

'That's right,' said Crippen, 'turn it up there, Michael, till we get another bit. It's better nor horse opera.'

'He talks massive,' said Mrs Brennan, 'you have to give him that.'

' . . . *and I'm glad to see they are all well muffled up, as they walk towards the quayside. This cold morning air can be quite sharp . . . '*

'I'd have sent over the loan of me shawl if I'd a known,' muttered

Maria.

'... *and they are, yes, they are, I'm sure they are shivering, though ever so slightly; this morning air from the sea, and a swell is rocking the vessel ever so slightly* ...'

'The cheek of it.'

'... *and I really think they are, in actual fact, I'm sure they have, or are going to, if they have not already, but I must really, now, pass you to my friend Redmond* ...'

'... *thank YOU, Cedric Hall-Ball, and now, briefly to recapitulate the journey out, some months ago, was the first they had flown in an aeroplane* ...'

'They usually flew in a wheelbarrow,' said Crippen.

'All the same,' said Mrs Brennan, 'it's a bit of gas, and I like to start the day with a bit of laugh. Good morning, all. We've to go as far as Candem Street.'

'We'll be out with you,' said the painter. 'I've to start out for this old one's ceiling in Foxrock.'

'And I've to buy a new ribbon for the old Remington.'

'Mark that judiciously, Maria,' said Mrs Brennan, 'he's to buy a new ribbon for his Renningtom.'

Irish Press 22 May 1954

Happy birthday to you

In our street general indignation was stirred by the case of Jack *versus* Saorstát Éireann, consequent upon Jack being put off the Labour by a hatch clerk, who had seen him march on the Gaiety stage as an Austro-Hungarian infantryman in the second act of *The Student Prince*. The hatch clerk, having seen him sign on that morning as an unemployed person, made a report and Jack's dole was stopped.

'I told him,' said Jack, 'that I was only appearing for the sake of art and the chance of lifting a white silk shirt, which as an Imperial Blaggard I wore as part of me get-up; but it was no use; he said it was employment within the meaning of the act, and me dole is stopped, and I'm being had up in Number Two Court in the case of Me *versus* Saorstát Éireann.'

'Sayers Todd Hernon,' muttered Lime Looney, grimly, 'that Bluff—in the law racket now, is he? There's a result. I knew him when he had nothing.

'Was it,' he stood up on his tippy-toes and raised his voice, 'was it for a scruff hound, and I can call him no less, like Sayers Todd Hernon to be swearing away the life of Jack?'

'See the Releeving Ovvicer, Jack,' said the Granny Nutty from a corner of the snug. 'I softened his cough.' She smiled reminiscently, or rearranged her wrinkles; the nearest thing to a smile you ever saw.

'The time they tried to stop a day's money on poor ould Winnie the Witch, because she missed a day's signing due to the ruffins in the room overhead hanging a sack over her window, so that she stopped in bed forty-eight hours not knowing night from day. That's who I'd see. Tell him,' she simpered, 'tell him I sent you.'

Now, many right-minded people are of the opinion that to walk on in *The Student Prince* for fifteen shillings a week, while getting nine shillings a week for signing on as an unemployed man, and thus making a total of one pound four shillings for a weekly income, is a great crime.

Most right-minded people, even in 1930, had an income many times one pound four shillings a week, but there weren't many of them knocking around our way.

We differed in opinion over some things to an extent of extreme spikery round about Armistice Day, when a riot was caused in Jimmy-the-Sports, by an ex-Dublin Fusilier telling a relative of mine that he had often seen a bigger row over beer in the canteen of a Saturday night, than a certain Tan war ambush in which this relative of mine had taken part.

My relative informed him that if he, the Fusilier, had killed any Germans, they were harmless ones to be killed be the likes of him that couldn't beat his way out of a paper bag.

But in the matter of Jack Rivers getting a few makes for walking on the stage in *The Student Prince*, and not losing two weeks' dole money by telling the Labour about his one week's work, we hadn't enough readies to enable us meet a just and moral conclusion—we were all for Jack.

All his fourteen children (even Lollie that was not much liked, since she clapped Chuckles Cleary on the back when he was blowing out a mouthful of paraffin oil on a lighted match) became great heroes, and when we saw the rozzers march down the road, we ran down the lane with them to hide them from Sayers Todd Hernon, who, I personally thought, was a well-dressed gentleman of exceptional ferocity, with apartments in Fitzgibbon Street Barracks and who dined off children whose fathers weren't working.

Sometimes when they had marched on in the direction of Croke Park, we'd let a shout after them:

'Harvey Duff, don't catch me,
Catch the fellow behind the tree'

and roar 'Up the Republic'. I wasn't sure why we roared 'Up the Republic', only to annoy the rozzers. I was sure that the Republic had not much time for Sayers Todd Hernon.

But before Jack's case came off there was an election, and TDs and would-be TDs of all and every political persuasion were being chased up the North Circular till they promised to 'look into the case'.

They did, and better than that, Jack got a job digging the Circular Road, at the Big Tree at Dorset Street, between Summerhill and the 'Joy' (if you've ever heard of that place), and arrived there with his pick and shovel as good as the next man.

At half past ten the foreman came up, looked at his watch, and nodded, at which the assembled Gaels bowed their heads low, and united their voices in:

'Happy birthday to you, happy birthday to you,
Happy birthday, happy birthday, happy birthday to you . . .'

Jack asked the more experienced Gael beside him whether it was the ganger's birthday.

'No,' says your man, 'but it's the second anniversary of the hole.'

Swine before the pearls

I read the middle page of the Irish edition of the *Sunday Express*, which was given over to the Beaverbrook prophet resident in this city. It was an article about Eamon de Valera and so full of '. . . smoke and stars', '. . . the dour black porter of the Celt', '. . . a Machiavellian mind for statesmanship', '. . . myth, mystery and legend', and Chinese laundry-keepers and even loyal sons of St Patrick, as to make one wonder whether its author is not in grave danger of meeting himself coming back.

There is more gas with the locals on the rest of the paper. Get on this, for instance; a letter to the editor.

I read in the 'Sunday Express' last week, that a woman fell into the Victoria Memorial fountain when the Queen was on the Palace balcony. I was that very wet person—or rather, one of the two who went in.
But who cared? I had seen our Queen and to see her was worth getting wet and an hour's journey home to dry clothes.
(Mrs) D. L—, N.9.
Mrs L—, fifty-one-year-old nurse, has been in love with royalty as long as she can remember. She has seen two Coronation processions, three Lyings-in-State, and most public functions attended by royalty during the last forty years.

The scribe, on the same page, has been hearing about the masque which undergraduates will stage for Princess Margaret's visit to the Oxford women's college, St Hilda's.

The masque *Porci ante Margaritan* has been specially written for the occasion.
The Princess will be greeted as 'Fairest of pearls, the world thine oyster', and will hear her astrological future foretold as:
Perhaps you will be meeting someone new,
Romance will very likely come to you.

Perhaps you will antagonise a friend,
But make it up, most likely, in the end.

   Miss Mann, principal of the college, saw the script and sent it to the Queen Mother. It was approved.

Translated, the masque's title is: *Swine before a Pearl.*

'My first was the very same. Poor Gonzaga Ignatius, "Hogger" I called him for a pet name,' said Mrs Brennan. 'Lost in the Boer War and never found. Lovely fellow, wasn't he, Maria?'

'Not tall enough to pick shamrock,' muttered Maria.

'All the same he was lovely in his little pillbox cap and his dotey little face with the big black moustache. You could nearly lift him up by it. And he was the very same about swine. Swine before pearls, or diamonds or anything.

'He'd get up in the middle of the night to eat swine, from the crubeen to the tip of the left ear.

'Swine before a pearl. Or before a pint. You couldn't beat his little hands away from this counter till he'd sunk twenty of them after a feed of pig's cheek.'

'God be with the days you'd get a head for two shillings and only newly married couples got a cheek between them,' sighed Maria.

'It's well I remember it,' said Mrs Brennan. 'Why wouldn't I and I married and a widow before I was eighteen.

'I was the champion widow of the quarter and if there was a widow's five-furlong sprint I'd have won it, with a length in hand, fifty years ago. For a long time I was betwixt and between, of course. Not knowing whether I was in it or out of it.'

'So?'

'And more so, Brending Behing. The War Office had no news of him for weeks, and thought he might have been a prisoner, and still alive. Though, in the heel of the hunt, we gave up all hope.'

She sniffed into the butt end of the tumbler.

'Ah, yes. When they found six Dubling Fusiliers' buttings in a lying's dem.'

'Them lions,' said Maria. 'You could never trust them.'

'And there was boings with the buttings.'

'Buttons and Bones,' said I.

'That's it,' said Mrs Brennan. 'Once they got the buttings and the boings, and God help poor little "Hogger", you'd have known his boings anywhere, they fixed me up with me pension.'

'Perhaps *you* will be meeting someone new,' I quoted.

'Ah, don't be talking. Didn't I meet him coming out of the 1906 Exhibishing? Just leaving the native village he was after leaving two dozen of large bottles and a quarter of brawn for the chief of the Royal Izumbis, and Earl of Addis Ababababababa, a chap be the name of Hogan, from Malpas Street.

'His father was a chef in O'Keefe's, the knacker's. Oh, indeed and I did meet someone new. Just like the man says in the poing.'

'I wrote a poem one time,' said Crippen.

'I wouldn't doubt you,' said I.

'And indeed I'm sure and you did, Mr Cripping, and it wouldn't be your best'

'Say a bit of it, so,' said Michael, from behind the counter.

Crippen glared angrily round, as poets do, and shouted, 'And sure, there yous are again, tormenting and annoying and persecuting me, because I trust a bit of me heart's core, a part of me pain, a bit of meself, a moment of me experience, pinned down in its trembling torture to the paper, like a butterfly to the board, yous meritless, jeering, sneering throng—'

'He's lovely,' sighed Mrs Brennan, 'like a mishing. Give the man a half, Michael. Go on now, Mr Cripping. Tell us the poing. As poor ould Tom Moore said, "Carry on with the coffing, the corpse'll walk."'

'All right, so,' said Crippen, watching with a sneer Michael fill out the half; 'mind your hand doesn't slip. I suppose there'll be neither peace nor ease, nor any kind of good left me, barring I reveal my soul and my hurt to yous.'

'A bit of order now,' said Mrs Brennan, 'and let the man show us his soul and his heart.'

Crippen lowered the half and projected his gaze far through Michael's window. Or to be precise, to the other side of East Arran Street, ten yards distant, the wall of the cabbage factory. He spoke in the agonised tones of one who had seen much, and didn't fancy any of it.

That's the way he spoke:

'There is a sadness in my sadness when I'm sad.
There is a gladness in my gladness when I'm glad.
There is a madness in my madness when I'm mad.
But the sadness in my sadness,
And the gladness in my gladness—'

'And the madness in your madness,' murmured Mrs Brennan respectfully.

'—Are nothing to my badness when I'm bad.'

There was a moment's silence and Mrs Brennan shook her head in the direction of the poet.

'Mr Cripping,' she sighed, 'you're rotting. Rotting with braings.'

Irish Press 19 June 1954

Here's how history is written and literature, for good measure

'He had a face like a plateful of mortal sins,' said the Bard.

'G'way,' said Crippen, 'you haven't a snap?'

'There wasn't much snaps going that time,' said the Bard, 'and our Provoke Sergeant, it was trying to forget him we were after we got away from him, not to be carrying round snaps or pictorial representations of him one way or another, except if he was swinging the wrong end of a rope. But that was the British Army for you, them times.'

'Well,' sighed Crippen, resignedly, 'to hear of a fellow the like of that, it'd kind of resign you to what me and me likes did to the same British Army afterwards. Aye, even if I done jail over it.'

'More luck to you,' muttered an old fellow, grimly, from the corner.

'Arrested, I was, at the Curragh races of 'twenty-one and charged with obtaining money by means of a trick—to wit, Find the Lady and The Sliced Woman—from a few Tommies that was only after

coming over for training.

'I took twenty-two bar off them, but pleaded in the court that we were entitled to some of our own back after all England robbed on us, and me solicitor said it was only plaguing the Egyptians, but the old beak said they weren't the Egyptians but the West Kents, and I got weighed off with six months. But I wasn't the only decent man in jail that time.'

'Bedad, you weren't,' said the old man, with a twisting of his gums. 'Aye, and many's the decent man was hung, and not a word about him.'

I struck up, to the air of 'The Rising of the Moon', and with vehemence:

'They told me, Francis Hinsley,
They told me you were hung . . .'

'Good on you,' said the old man, his hand on his ear, for fear he'd miss one word.

'With red protruding eyeballs . . .'

'More luck to me one son,' said the old man, in tears of content.

'. . . and black protruding tongue.'

'Ah, your blood's worth bottling,' screeched the old man.

'Is that one of Yeets's?' asked Crippen.

'No, that was written by Evelyn Waugh,' said I.

'And bedad and she wasn't a bad one, either,' said Crippen, shaking his head. '"I'll dress myself in man's attire and fight for liberty", what? Eveleen was far from being the worst. What was this crowd she was with, now? I just can't think of it for the minute.'

'Wasn't it the Belcuddy Battalion, or the First Battalion of the Third Belcuddy Brigade?' said I. 'You should know that, Crip, above anyone.'

He spat on the floor and looked seriously round the company. 'Not a man in Ireland should know better.'

'What part of the country would that be now?' asked the Bard, who is himself a native of the far north, Ballymoney direction.

'What part of the country?' asked Crippen, incredulously. 'Is it coddin me y'are, or what?'

He looked over at the old man.

'Can you believe your ears? A man here does not know where,' he paused a minute. 'Er . . . eh . . .'

'Belcuddy,' said I.

'That's right,' said Crippen. 'Belcuddy is.'

The old man looked over and waved his stick: '*Ná bac leis*. Leave him to God!'

Crippen fixed the Bard with a severe look.

'Certainly. I'd a thought anyone would a known that. Nawbocklesh. It's about eight miles this side of it. Nice little town, too.' His lips softened in a reminiscent smile. 'Nawbocklesh,' says he, 'and the blue sky over it.'

Crippen sighed, and the old man gazed on the floor, thinking of old times, and ground his gums together with a noise like a sand lorry on the mountain road outside.

I raised my eyes to the ceiling and opened my mouth in a patriotic fashion:

'Oh, down in Belcuddy they fought the glorious fight,
All through the day and through most of the night,
And never knocked off, for sup, bit or bite . . .'

'Ah, me good-living youth,' said the old man.

'Ah, there was great men in the country that time,' said Crippen.

'Aye, and women, too, like the one that wrote the bit of a song your gills there was singing.'

'Is it Eveleen Warr?' asked my gills.

'The very woman. The Bardess of Belcuddy, we called her.' He looked at the Bard. 'You and her might have made a match of it. Set up in the bard line together. But I believe she was sweet on the Commandant and when he got killed in the Butter Tasting and Poultry Station, she never did an hour's good. It's all in a poem she wrote, the time of the death:

"I leave up me Thompson, and me short Webley,
Distribute me hand grenades among the foe,
I'm fed up fighting for dear old Ireland,
And to a convent I now will go."

'A lovely thing that.'

Irish Press 26 June 1954

Pity the poor man on the road to Carlisle

Besides the Bard, Crippen, myself and Mrs Brennan, there was a duffel-coat in the corner containing, newly arrived off the Liverpool boat, a young Irish poet of uncertain age.

'No,' said Crippen, in answer to Mrs Brennan, 'he's not a monk. That's a poet's get-up he has on. And he leans his head on his hands because it saves his energy for writing poems and roaring at the people. I'll just see if he's in form yet.'

'Ask him if he knows that one o' Burns, "Hoo Crool",' said the Bard.

Crippen went towards the recumbent form of the YIP and shook it. He looked round at the people and said, 'This is like a poem of Burns' and all, "The Wind that Shakes the Duffel-Coat".'

'God forgive you, Mr Cripping,' said Mrs Brennan, 'you're a deeming.'

The duffel-coat shook itself and the Young Irish Poet shook himself and glared at us with the fury of a newly woken squirrel.

'Do I know?' he screamed. 'Do I know? Woe! An ignorant, meritless crew are you—'

'I told you, Bard,' said Crippen, 'he'd leave you in the ha'penny place. Words at will he has, rhymed and ready.'

'—crew are you. That never as much as glanced at the last issue of *The Blunt Instrument*, the last of the little reviews with the fifth of my cantos in it:

"Woe, there is a lot of it, flying round,
More often the sound, sniff, sniff,
Of woe,
Than any of your damned ha, ha, ha, or
Hoe, hoe, hoe."'

He slumped back in his duffel-coat and waved the back of his hand to us before submerging again.

'Massive,' said Mrs Brennan; 'especially the cursing at the end.'

'Fine fellow,' said Crippen, 'You want to read a poem he wrote one time called "Where Am I?" Took a degree in knowledge at the National University, Trinity College, Dublin! Never did a day's work in his life, but a lovely dancer.'

'Burns was the very same,' said the Bard.

'Oh, the very same,' said Crippen. 'You know, the bit where he says:

"You may hay the growsy or the grunk,
But a mon's a mon, a mon, a mon, a mon,
An hay ye don't like it, I no care,
To me, it's all the one."'

'I don't recall that bit,' said the Bard.

'And hard for you,' said Crippen, 'for it was never let out to the ordinary public. 'Case the other crowd would be made as wise as themselves. But I got it from the right quarter; chap in the gas company. That's all fine and large, but I'm telling you that it's not what you know but who you know; and a shut mouth will catch no flies; better to be mean than at a loss, have you me?'

'There's a lot in what you say,' said the Bard. 'I mind the time I was in Dumfries. When I was in the Army.' 'Was in a Scotch regiment myself,' said Crippen, 'the Submarine Kilties. Deserted the time of the Economic War. Wouldn't sell my own ould country. Besides, they started giving us New Zealand mutton.'

'Well, this was in the First War. I was after coming over from Larne, through Portpatrick, and enlisted in a moment of foolishness in the Scotch Terriers. They were a guid enough mob—they called them the "Dogs of War"—but the Provoke Sergeant—'

'The one with the face like a plateful of mortal sins?' asked Crippen.

'The very same,' said the Bard.

'Well,' said Crippen, 'just so as we'd know him.'

'I was left minding the canteen one night, an' what happened but I left a tap running when I'd fallen asleep. And there was nearly a hogshead short and the Provoke Sergeant wakes me up and says I was under close arrest and I could take me choice of being tried under military law and being shot for deserting my post by falling asleep under the barrel, or being tried under civil law and hung for sacrilege.

'To give me time to consider me position I was locked up in the guardroom, which was a wee place with a window looking down into the barrack yard thirty feet below.

'I looked around me and there was nothing in the guardroom but a water-jug, table and stool and a cupboard in the wall. There was nothing in the cupboard when I looked but a lot of rifle pull-throughs, lengths of cloth, three feet long. And I had an idea of a sudden.

'There was eleven of them. That meant thirty feet and something over for the knots. I could make a rope. No sooner said than done.

'I made me rope, attached one end to the window, slid down and over the wall and was on the road to Carlisle before you could say—'

'Mull o' Galloway,' said Crippen.

'But when I got to the border between Annan in Scotland and Longtown in England, what do I see but a sentry-box blocking me way to Carlisle and the London road and me with no papers. But I sneaks up beside the box and rubs me feet on the road, and the sentry shouts out, "Halt, who goes there?"

'I said it was me, and he shouts at me like he's talking to a half-fool: "And where do you think you're going this hour of the night?"

'"If you please sir, I want to get to Scotland. I live in Annan, and me mother will be worried about me."

'"You should have thought of that before twelve o'clock. Get back there, to the English side now, for your mother will have to do without you until morning. Come on now," he says, waving the rifle at me. "Get back there, and if I catch you trying to sneak into Scotland past this post, I'll put one through you, you loon, you."

'And he puts me on down the road and I'm safe and sound on the way to Carlisle.

'Till I got very tired after all the walking and sat down on an empty box on wheels, a sort of a watch-box, to rest myself, and was only woken up by a low and savage growling, like a beast of prey.'

'The Provoke Sergeant?' said Crippen.

'No,' said the Bard, 'but what was nearly as bad. A ferocious-looking watch-dog.'

'An Allegation,' said Mrs Brennan.

'There was only one thing to be done. Grab a hold of his tail. I manoeuvred round as best I could till at last I got a grip on it, and he let a roar and a howl out of him like the Zoo on strike, but I held on till he tried to run away from me, and the watch-box went along on its wheels on the road, and the harder he pulled to get away from me, the tighter I gripped, till he drew me on the watch-box the whole way to Carlisle.

'Then, just as dawn rose over the spires of the town, I let go of the dog and he dropped down dead.'

Irish Press 3 July 1954

Sermons in cats, dogs—and mice

There is a collection of essays in the Penguin series called *Music At Night*. They were written by Aldous Huxley about twenty years ago. Although a Penguin-educated citizen myself, I read this book a lot of years ago before it was in Penguins, at a time when I was leading a more contemplative life and had plenty of time to think about what I read.

One of the essays deals with the next world, and what we are likely to be doing in it, and is called 'Squeak and Gibber'.

I was thinking of the essay Huxley calls 'Sermons in Cats'.

A man wishing to be a writer wants Huxley to tell him the best way to go about it. Now don't think I'm going to set up in an advisory capacity on this matter.

Seán Ó Faoláin, father confessor, nursemaid, and prison visitor to some of my grade, used to say that the equipment of a writer should consist of pen, paper, and a time-sheet. To write, and see that you wrote a certain amount every day. And a ledger to note what you sent out in the way of MSS, and what you got for them.

Huxley advises your man to watch cats. They live and love, are jealous, mean, generous, and all to that effect.

He says that the man to whom he gave this advice did not seem very grateful for it.

I'd have picked up a cat and hit him a belt of it. Only I happen to like cats.

For his advice was rubbishy, and there is nothing about human beings that cannot be learned better from human beings than from any other creature that lives on earth.

The man who said that the more he saw of mankind, the more he liked his dog, was some species of informer or handman's labourer, that his own mother would run away from, could she but lose him in a big enough crowd.

And the dog was the leavings of a lurcher that only stopped with him because he was too weak with the hunger for his legs to carry him any more than two yards in the one day.

'I'll never forget our poor ould bowler,' said Mrs Brennan. 'Poor ould Pram. Poor faithful ould K-mine.'

'What's mine?'

'K-mine. I don't like calling him a brute. I know they've no souls, but you never know what he might be in another world listening to us. Not but what,' she added significantly, 'but what they might be as well entitled to souls as certain individgeyoulums I know.'

'That'll do you now,' said Crippen. 'None of your theology. This is a respectable house.'

Mrs Brennan, lost in a mournful recollection, sighed. 'Ah, poor ould Pram.'

'Pram?' said I.

'That's right. We called him "Pram" after the dog that belonged to Fill Mac Coon.'

Cats are not know-alls. They are independent enough, and nobody ever saw a cat at one end of a lead and a policeman at the other. Belloc says they are of the breed of the devil and cannot be poisoned. Too often this has been disproved.

People (for some reason of the would-be yokel variety) like to hang their tongues, village-idiot fashion, and tell you how they cannot stick cats.

'Well,' my mother's first mother-in-law would say, 'd'you prefer rats?'

Leaving that to one side, cats have their rights as well as anyone under the constitution of this State, and it's a punishable offence to put them into areas in the new converted Corporation flats, so that they're trapped and die of starvation and thirst after days of agony.

The older people in those parts know that only for the cats we'd never have survived in those rat-warrens. Children growing up in better times may not realise this.

That is the point of this sermon. And if they don't they take it to heart, I know certain little devils that will be getting a kick where it won't blind them.

The late Sister Monica, who taught generations of boys, including Seán Russell, and one of the editors of the *Irish Digest* and the present writer, at North William Street School, was encouraging a boy called Champers, who, even for that district, was considered a chaw of some dimensions. Some doubted whether he was a human being at all, and by his shaggy looks and his taste for raw vegetables and chewing tobacco he might have escaped from a circus.

Champers, by dint of much pen-chewing, finally produced a composition: 'The Autobiography of a Mouse'.

'I was a muss. So was me mother and me father and we all et chees till the cat kem an et me da an me ma an me an all.'

'Now, Stanislaus Kostka'—this was Champers' real name—'that is really very good indeed and most interesting, but,' and Sister Monica looked at him earnestly from under her big linen bonnet, 'if the mouse was eaten by the cat, how could he have written his autobiography?'

Champers looked at her scornfully, and asked with great patience, 'Listen, Sister, how could a mouse write his beeyografee anyway?'

Irish Press 24 July 1954

Meet a great poet

'Brending Behing.'

'Good morning, Mrs Brennan.'

'And good luck.'

'As the crow said to the duck.'

'You too, Maria, and your friends in America.'

'What I want to know is, where might you be going with the Rennington? Not a visit to your uncle, so early in the morning?'

'There's much value in scrap these days,' muttered Crippen, from a corner. He has literary ambition himself and bitterly resents any pretensions in that direction on the part of anyone else. The sight of my battered old typewriter is a cause of severe illness to him. If I wanted to see him jump off Butt Bridge, I'd only have to walk down East Arran Street carrying a brief-case.

'Ah, I don't know now,' said Maria, with an amiable sniff.

'I know you don't,' said Crippen. 'I heard all about you. When the white gas meters came out, you were an hour trying to get into the *Balladmakers' Saturday Night* on your one.'

'Ah now, Mr Cripping. Maria's not all that bad. She can count her change lovely if whatever it is she's buying hasn't gone up from the last time she bought it. We can't all be cheenises like yourself and Brending Behing there.'

'And if you want to know,' said I, 'I'm taking this machine to be cleaned and oiled.'

'And it's not all that bad of a machine, Mr Cripping. Do you not remember the testimoleum he did for poor Henrietta on it?'

'I do not,' said Crippen.

'Ah, don't you remember? He came here one morning and poor Henrietta, she used to follow painters, cleaning houses and washing up their dirt after them, before she took to the lifting, and then she wasn't able to get a job on account of not having a testimoleum, and where would she get it, barring they'd give her one out of the Joy, but Brending Behing here sat down in the corner, opened up the yoke and there and then wrote her a beauty of a reverence.

'You'd have got yourself a job on the strent of it. To the effect that she was the nanny of his children till they were big enough to beat her, and he knew that she was a life-long teetotaller and a lovely knitter, with a soft hand under a duck, and to who it might concern and them it didn't, could go and do the other, and it had his signature and all to it. What was it now? Lord Williamstown and Booterstown and Monkstown and . . .'

'Blanchardstown,' suggested Maria, helpfully.

'And she got a lovely position with some old one from England, took everything that wasn't nailed down, only they caught her carrying out the sundial. Very unlucky thing to be caught with.'

'I know this much,' said Crippen, 'if I was doing me writing, I couldn't do it on one of them things.'

'God knows and you're right there, Mr Cripping. I'd like to see the bookies, the day of a big race, and everyone trying to write their three cross-doubles and the same back, on them things. All them machines going together you'd think it was the Hammond Lane you were in, and how would a body hear a result or anything?'

'I wasn't talking about writing three cross-doubles,' said Crippen, crossly.

'Well, accumalators, wouldn't they be worse, and—'

'I was talking about writing poetry,' said Crippen, in some exasperation. I mean, looking as if bad words would be sullying his lips any minute.

'Oh, yes, Mr Cripping. Now I have you.'

He looked sternly at me. 'Tell me any great poem that was written on one of them things?'

'Well,' said I, 'I was going to say that I didn't stand over the shoulders of great poets to know what way they went about it.'

'Well, well,' quoted Crippen, 'that's what you look for when the beer runs out. But you can't answer me. And remember I wrote poems before you come up. *And* translations from the English language, the Irish language . . .'

'The deaf and dumb language,' offered Maria.

'I didn't know you wrote Irish,' said I.

'You didn't know. You didn't know because you never went to the trouble of finding out.'

'Well, say one now, Mr Cripping; go on, say it up now and the divil thank the begrudgers.'

'I'll say it, though seeing as yous don't understand the language yous won't be much the better of it.'

He looked round at the audience and fixed Maria with an arrogant glance. 'Like a sow looking into a swill barrel,' he muttered elegantly.

'I know a bit of Irish,' said I.

'You do, but it's only the new stuff they have in the schools. Dots and dashes. But this is the real goat's toe.'

He cleared his throat and began:

Phillaloo, wirrastroo,
Sure I'm kilt,
May the quilt
Rest lightly on your beautiful form,
When the weather is hot, or'

(he waved a complacent hand)

'Again when it's not,
I'll roll you up,
Cosy and warm.'

'That's massive,' said Mrs Brennan. 'Have you e'er another one? I could folly nearly every word of that.'

'This one is a lot harder.'

'Well, never mind, it's all for the cause. Me poor father had a lovely poen called, "Never Hit a Lady With Your Hat On", but it was only English.'

'Hhhhm,' said Crippen, clearing his throat and throwing out his hand in declamation:

'Come out, my shillelagh,
Come out, love, to me,
On the bright Cruiskeen Lawn
We will dance the Banshee;
And while bright shines the moon,

Lady Luna above,
In the groves of Na Bocklesh
We'll lovingly rove.
And softly and sweetly I'll murmur to you,
Musha and allanna, astore, tiggin too.'

'Massive,' muttered Mrs Brennan, rubbing her eye. 'Oh, leave it to you, Mr Cripping!'

But going out, Michael called me and said out of the side of his mouth, 'He never made them poems up.'

'No?'

''Course he didn't. They were written by Yeets. Y'often heard of him; owned the Half-Way House above in Drimnagh.'

Irish Press 31 July 1954

From Dublin to les Champs Elysées

Paris, as the man said, *est toujours Paris*. Always her own sweet self. She looks much the same as usual, except for the fact that the Metro has gone up to thirty francs and the Government of Mendés-France gets a little less abuse than previous governments.

The talk about local politicians and other notabilities in a Paris bistro is like a breath of home to the Dubliner, far from the scurrilities of pub conversation in his native city, and just as intimately savage. So, it will be seen that the present government of France is enjoying a summer of great popularity.

Thirty francs is about eightpence, and, for a short journey, is fairly dear. But once you buy a ticket you are at liberty to go anywhere the Metro goes, and it will take you right from one end of the city to the other.

For a worker living in Belleville, and working in Montrouge, say, which would be as far as from Kimmage to Dún Laoghaire, it is not much dearer than CIE.

The buses are dearer than the underground, and are much less comfortable and up-to-date than ours. They are all single deckers, and when I went to Paris after the war, I was told that there was a shortage of buses, the Germans having taken a great number of them with them on the retreat of 1944.

Judging by the length of time I waited for a number ninety-five, in the Avenue de l'Opéra, they must not have given them back yet.

Though, looking up at the destination board on the lamp-post, I felt I could forgive a lot to a vehicle that made regular journeys to places like Saint-Germain-des-Prés, the Louvre, and Carrousel.

Saint-Germain-des-Prés or south side of the Seine, on the Left Bank, is to the post-war intellectual, genius or phoney, have it whatever way you like, what Montmartre was to the artist of Picasso's youth, before the first war and, as a refuge of sinners, has succeeded Montparnasse, stamping-ground of Hemingway and Scott Fitzgerald in the 'twenties.

It gained notoriety as the headquarters of Jean-Paul Sartre, just after the Liberation. He had a flat on the corner of the Rue Bonaparte, and the adjoining licensed premises, the Deux Magots and the Flore, became the twin cathedrals of existentialism, of which philosophy he is the high priest.

As regards 'existentialism', see the more learned literary page of this journal. Try MacManus, Kiely or Williams. I am doing my best for you when I pass on Cecil Ffrench Salkeld's definition of it. He said it teaches that 'man is sentinel to the null'.

And as good an excuse for robbing all round you as any other, as Monsieur Jean Prevet has proved, with great profit for himself.

This man was a burglar for many years, and also a poet. He was arrested many times for breaking and entering, and each time refused to recognise the court. Like Marlowe, who countered all objection to home production of coin of the realm with the remark that he was as much entitled to mint money as the Queen of England, Monsieur Prevet told the court that he robbed as an existentialist, and had a conscientious objection to keeping his hands easy.

In a less civilised country, he would now be engaged in the production of mailbags, four stitches to the inch. But Sartre, and a number of other writers, demanded that they leave the boy alone. And he is now an honoured French writer, a credit to his country, and the proprietor of an estate in the country.

He doesn't need to do any more work in the burglaring line, and lives on the proceeds of his books.

I had extracts of his autobiography read to me, some of which rose the hair on my head. And, as my mother once remarked, that which would shock Brendan Behan, would turn thousands grey.

Oscar Wilde died in a hotel down the street, in the Rue d'Alsace, and tradition has it that it was a priest of Saint-Germain-des-Prés Church attended him on his death bed.

The first thing one learns on visiting Paris, is that it is not what it was. I was told that some years ago, and for the first time was able to pass that remark to some Irish students half a generation younger than myself.

I do not really believe it, though things are a bit dearer. A hotel room is five hundred francs a night, which is ten shillings and not much, if you think in terms of Galway race week, but twice as much as six or seven years ago.

Old Raymond Duncan, who ran an Akademia of Greek culture in the Rue Dauphine, is either dead or in America.

Time was when I watched him, in the midst of his disciples, elderly ladies and gentlemen dressed in blankets, and sandals, a sort of kilted costume that bore as much resemblance to the clothes of the ancient Greeks as the uniform of the Fintan Lalor Pipe Band to that of Brian Boru, in solemn procession, to greet the dawn at the bottom of our street on midsummer morn.

With what ecstasy I saw them trip over a wire thoughtfully provided by the boys of the Beaux Arts and stretched ankle high across the road. God be with the youth of us, the simple pleasures of the poor.

The Bonapartist, who used to march along the Boulevard Saint-Germain in his long coat and cocked hat, sword ever at the ready to

[32]

avenge the slightest insult to his Emperor, was no longer in evidence; nor was Confucius, an old Chinaman or something, who specialised in one branch of English literature, and that a bilingual catalogue from Messrs Whiteleys of London of which he would read you a couple of hundred pages so that you might know how 'three-piece Chesterfield suite, twenty pounds ten,' or 'oak double bed, eleven pounds, ten shillings; mattress, best flock extra,' sounded in Chinese.

And dare you move an inch till the last huckaback towel was disposed of, for he was a man of wide culture and, in addition to his literary talents, was a ju-jitsu expert.

But the Pergola is still open, 'jour et nuit,' and its proprietor, still large and affable, and very wide awake behind the bar, though he could hardly have got to sleep since the last time I was there.

He remembered me and shook me warmly by the hand when I went in. He asked me how I was, and how long I expected to be around this time.

I told him I was off to the Riviera in the morning, and he smiled even more cordially, and did not seem at all upset at the prospect of my departure after so short a visit. He remembered me, all right.

Irish Press 7 August 1954

The road to Lyons—the poet Yeats disliked parsnips

On the boat from Newhaven I met three Queen's University students, who were also bound for the South of France.

The train costs about seven pounds from Paris to Cannes, and though I knew how to get a fruit lorry from Les Halles market, for a couple of thousand francs, that sort of travelling does not appeal to me any more. I would sooner leave it to the boy scouts and to An Óige.

So when these fellows told me that they knew of a bus service, that took you to Cannes for less than four pounds, food and lodging included, I gladly availed myself of the information.

At four o'clock in the morning, I decided it was too late to bother getting a hotel, and as it was a pity to break up the company, my friends announced that they would stick it out, till it was time to get the auto-bus, which left the Rue l'Arcade at seven o'clock.

So we had another couple, just to show no coolness, and settled down in the Pergola, for another couple of hours. An American, upon being introduced, and being told I was from Dublin, asked me if I had known James Joyce. I regretted that I did not have that honour, but told him that my mother had cooked a meal for W. B. Yeats in Madam MacBride's house in Stephen's Green, and that the poet turned up his nose to the parsnips.

'He did not like parsnips?' said the American, reaching for a notebook. 'You're sure this is factual?'

'It is to be hoped,' I replied, 'that you are not calling my mother a liar.'

'No, no, of course not. But she might have been mistaken. Maybe it was carrots,' he added hastily.

'You must think I'm a right thick to have a mother that can't tell a carrot from a parsnip.'

'No, certainly not. I'm sure you wouldn't. I mean I'm sure she could. But this is very important.' He wrote in the book. 'Parsnips, attitude of Yeats to.' 'And you say he didn't like Stephen's Greens, either. Now what sort of vegetables are they?'

At this point the patron introduced a Belgian to me, who shook me warmly by the hand and said he knew my country well. In connection with an American construction company during the war, he had twice visited Reykjavik. With some relief, I got back to my vegetable man.

When we went out to get the Metro for my auto-bus to the sun, the dawn was as bleak as a summer's morning at home. I got my ticket, got aboard the coach and fell asleep. I did not wake up until we were going past Fontainebleau. My companions were a Belgian, whom I questioned closely about his wartime activities till I had satisfied myself that they had not taken him to Reykjavik, and two young Frenchmen.

Further up the coach I heard a strong Lancashire voice, and in the course of the journey, discovered it belonged to a little man from Preston, which, he told me (proudly), has the reputation of being 'poor, proud, and Papist'.

At Avignon, we walked around the Pope's palace, in a proprietorial fashion, before refreshing ourselves with a couple of rossiners. Very good red wine, of course, at about twopence a glass.

I was about to remark that a country with such beautiful drink and a hundred and twenty different sorts of cheese, was still well worth a visit, when my companion wiped his lips and spoke.

'Desperate stuff, isn't it? Ee, it's like vinegar. And that there crawling muck they call cheese. Why, a man'd be run in, in England for even possessing the like of that, much less selling it. A danger to public 'ealth, I'd call it.'

'It's shocking all right,' said I, wondering where I'd buy a litre of wine and a box of Camembert or a bit of Brie for the trip to Aix-en-Provence. Luckily, I'd be in the back of the car, and he'd not see me devouring it. 'We might as well have another, though, seeing as we can get nothing else. Garçon, encore de rouge, s'il vous plait.'

I knocked it back, as best I could, and my companion looked at me suspiciously.

'You swallowed that like you liked it,' said he.

'Best to get it over, quickly,' said I, 'it's good for warts.'

Our bus was parked by a Roman Arch, like a miniature Arc de Triomphe, the father and mother of all arches of triumph, including the Marble Arch, and the arch at the top of Grafton Street, which commemorates Ireland's victory over the Boers, or the foundation stone of Wolfe Tone's memorial, removed, as an obstruction, by police order.

But it was only when we got to Lyons that my mind began to run on the wrongs of the dead, for it was here I discovered that my ticket did not cover hotel expenses. I should have known that. Four pounds is not much for a journey twice the length of Ireland, but like many another, the Dubliner is the victim of his own prejudices.

Conditioned all the days of my life, to the belief that people from the three other provinces, Cork, the North and the Country, could build nests in your ear, mind mice at a crossroads, and generally stand where thousands fell, I implicitly accepted the word of these Northern fellows, who had never set foot in France before, against my better judgement, and lived riotously all the way from Dieppe to this Lyons, where we were heartlessly dislodged from our seats and put out on the road, to get hotels we had not the money for.

Still, it was some consolation, to see the three Queen's men walk abjectly towards the river bank.

'The mon says we have to find our own hotel,' said their leader, miserably, 'and it just doesn't run it.'

'The Rhône is first turn on your right,' said I, and walked on considerably cheered. Besides, I remembered that I know a journalist in the place.

On a visit to Dublin I had arranged for him to meet the leader of the Irish underground, a chap that worked in a basement store, and he had asked me to call in any time I was passing.

Irish Press 14 August 1954

Terror in the Alps of France

I Alped my way, for some weary hours, till the sun went down and I found myself alone in the mountain sand in the dark.

I remembered a book we had at school called *Seilg I measc na nAilp*, or *A Hunt in the Alps*, and when I saw a bright light appear and reappear in front of me, wondered with something approaching terror, as they say in books, whether I might be the object of this one.

A hoarse barking, as if in suppressed rancour and not all that suppressed, broke on my ears, and I started to run. But it was not much use running, for the light appeared in my path and the grunting bark grew louder, and anyway it was too far to run to Dolphin's Barn.

Not all the sins of my past life passed in front of me, but as many as could get room in the queue. Not since I slept in a barn at a place called Rambouillet, the other end of France, next to a horse that mended his own shoes in the small hours of the morning, was I so frightened.

I struggled on in this alien wilderness, and for company's sake thought of King Daithi, killed at the foot of the Alps. Why did not anyone ever warn both of us to keep out of them?

The light appeared again and the barking kept on, and it was better than a Mission. I sweated about seven pounds till a car came round the corner and caught me in the headlights.

It stopped and I never heard brakes go on with greater pleasure. I mean, never with greater pleasure did I hear brakes go on. I was in no humour for worrying about my prose style at that moment. I didn't care if it was Dracula himself driving that heap of scrap, only to hear a semi-human voice and know there were other ways of communication beside this barking-grunting.

It wasn't Dracula—at least if it was he was not in uniform—but a man on his way home from work.

'C'est le route à Montcolin?' I asked.

He said it was the road to Montcolin and, what was better, that he would give me a lift to within a couple of miles of Montcolin.

'May your shadow never grow less, O man of the van,' said I with fervour and got into it.

I staggered into the Irish encampment, a villa high in the mountains, in the small hours of the morning, and was fed and given drink, and related my story. I spoke of the lights and the barking.

My host laughed.

'Those lights were fireflies. And the barking you heard was the grunting of the frogs.'

'Why, of course,' said I; 'how silly of me.' But I had never experienced anything the like of that on Sundrive Road.

Time heals all things and I woke up twelve hours later as good as ever I was. The village of Montcolin is shortly to become famous over Radio Éireann and you will know more about it than many of its inhabitants, and certainly more than anyone outside it, for it is locked high up in the Alpes Maritimes.

We went down to Cannes by car and swam in the Mediterranean.

At Juan les Pins, Sugar Ray Robinson was performing in the Hollywood night-club, where a beer would cost you something in the region of a pound, if they sold you one, which they would if you were wealthy enough.

The usual drink is champagne, but I was told of an American in a hotel who wanted a cola with his lunch.

Colas are popular in France, but this hotel did not stock it, so a waiter was sent round the corner to buy one from a stall for fifty francs and twenty on the bottle.

The cola was duly bought and taken on a tray with ice and a napkin round the neck, to the gentleman, who drank it, expressed himself pleased with its quality, and cheerfully paid eight hundred francs for it (sixteen shillings), plus two hundred service, which made it the even quid.

The man that sold it to the waiter told me and he was told by the waiter, when the waiter came back for the twenty francs refund on the bottle.

We went to our beach, which was called the Rio, and there, for the day, you could hire a seat and a parasol to shade you when you were out of the water, for a couple of shillings. You could get a quart bottle of iced beer for about one-and-ninepence, and, best of all, you had the whole shimmering sea from there to Africa for nothing.

They also had for hire a kind of paddle-boat in which you sat and propelled yourself by a sort of pedal action on the same principle as a bicycle. I heard that people had tried to pedal to Corsica on them, though why they weren't satisfied with where they were is beyond me.

Myself and a gang of kids, Irish, Anglo-Irish, Dutch-Irish and Russian-Irish, got in, and it would have taken a bayonet charge by the First Battalion to get us out.

There is no swimming till you swim in water like that. No breaking the ice. No diving in to 'put yourself out of pain' as we used to say in Dollymount. Just a matter of languidly rambling out till you are into it and alive again, after being comfortably comatose in the sun.

I cannot understand why very small children when swimming on your back, cannot get the idea of holding on to your shoulders, rather than half strangling you by the firm pressure of baby hands on your windpipe. Still, we enjoyed it.

I was more than repaid for the perils of the deep when I heard the smallest and most lethal one reply, when someone asked from the beach whether she wanted her big rubber raft: 'We don't want the wubber waft. We got Bwendan.' So she had, in a drowning man's grip, though I lived to tell the tale.

Talking about Dollymount, reminds me of when I was at school.

The teacher, one Monday morning, came in, and said that she had been at Killiney the previous day, but that she had not enjoyed it, the place was crowded with trippers.

I had very little idea of what she was talking about but, like Lanna Machree's dog, I'd go a bit of the road with anyone.

'Dollymount is the very same, miss,' said I. 'Them trippers. Place is rotten with them.'

She looked at me incredulously. 'But—but Dollymount is for trippers.'

I'm a tripper here, and so is nearly everyone else. Just a tourist, though it's a word of loathing to most of the English-speaking foreigners.

There is an American cartoon that shows a man, with strawbainer hat, camera, blazer and flannels, and he is saying to his wife:

'I look like a tourist. I am a tourist. So what?'

I wouldn't mind being left like that.

Irish Press 28 August 1954

These alien monuments—thoughts before the Albert Memorial

I was reared in the belief that the greatest disaster that ever befell mankind was the defeat of Napoleon at the battle of Waterloo. That it opened a century of unparalleled misery for the people of Ireland, and that the little corporal, even at his most cynical, was a more civilised figure than the licensed thug, and loud-mouthed head bailiff, whose victories on behalf of European reaction, and the privileges of land-lords, are commemorated in the Phoenix Park.

Bonaparte's royalist pretensions and imperial lunacies were more worthy of a talentless, dull, race of well-to-do nail and saucepan merchants, depending upon the revelations of homely native bodies about an imported royalty to give a bit of colour to their lives. And they ruined him, but at least he is remembered by the Code Napoleon, and the straight roads he built.

Wellington, the made-in-Brummagen Iron Duke, if he is remembered for any law, it is the Poor Law, if for any building, it is the workhouse.

As for the obelisk in the Park, it was put there by the enemies of the people of Ireland, and should be shifted, now that they are no longer powerful enough to enforce its preservation.

Neither has the Martyr of the Pillar any claim on our consideration. As Bernard Shaw said, he won victories he'd have been deservedly shot for losing, and anyway has nothing to do with us.

One occasionally hears about the attachment of the 'old Dubliner' to these objects, but in this case the 'old Dubliner' is usually some immigrant employee of the Castle or one of the banks, that came over as a trustworthy messenger about fifty years ago, and has only as much right as any other Irish citizen, to debate the matter.

The oldest Dubliners, the descendants of the native Irish, that crept in and settled round Ballybough (an Baile Bocht—'the poor town'), regarded the Wellington Monument and the Pillar as a gibe at their own helplessness in their own country.

I remember, as a very small child, travelling with a grand-aunt of mine. She was born and reared at Blessington Street, near the Basin, formerly the City Reservoir, and whose waters, she claimed, were cleaner and purer and better for making tea than the 'new stuff' from Roundwood.

We sat in a tram, and listened to an elderly gentleman inquire of the conductor whether the tram went to 'Kingstown'.

The conductor replied in even tones that he did not know of the existence of any such place.

The old gent with some impatience replied that the place, with the chopping and changing of modern times, was now called something else, 'er—Done-Lakery or some such.'

This bit of fencing, the old gent pretending he did not know how to pronounce 'Dún Laoghaire' and the conductor pretending he had never heard of 'Kingstown', continued till at last, to cut a long story short, it was decided that he was on the right tram.

'Of course,' said the old gent, 'it was called Kingstown by the old people.'

'Excuse yourself,' said my grand-aunt, 'excuse yourself, sir. I don't know how old you are, but I'm nearly eighty, and I never heard it called anything but Dunleary. I don't know how long you're in the city, sir, but my mother, who stayed with friends in Glasthule every summer, went to her grave without ever knowing it was called anything else.'

I was thinking about all this as I walked through Hyde Park. Till I stood before the Albert Memorial, I never knew how much we had to be thankful for in the matter of nineteenth-century British memorials.

On a broad base surrounded by stone elephants, stone mahouts, stone Red Indians, and other inhabitants of his wife's empire, there rises to a point, sixty or seventy feet above the lowest stone moccasin, a sort of shrine, the centre of which can be best described as a Gothic watch-box, where your man crouches, sheltering from the rain.

His young wife stands waving to him from outside Kensington Palace, in sculpture executed by her daughter, a young German princess, who'd have been better advised to stick to her own business of kissing kangaroos and dancing with the Maoris.

It is a bit difficult to believe that the native language of this mortuary, could they but speak, would be German, and that after the Prussian victory at Sedan in 1870, the royal family assembled at the chapel in Windsor to give thanks for the victory in a prayer composed by another artistic princess whose bent was for literature.

'Let's join our heart with cousin Bill,
And praise the heavens, with a will,
Ten thousand Frenchmen sent below
Praise God from whom all blessings flow.'

I remember many years ago a preacher of Irish revolt, in Hyde Park. His following seemed more personal than organisational, but he did not lack support for all that. He was very fond of demanding: 'D'you think I done fifteen years in Maryboro, for nothing?'

This silenced all interrupters, except on one occasion when a man with a similar accent to the speaker, replied with easy familiarity: 'You did not then, Tom, 'twas for pushing a boy into the Shannon. You were a lucky man you weren't hung.'

Irish Press 16 October 1954

We took over a castle

You may find it hard to believe that I was ever an invited guest in a castle, but in my childhood I spent a great number of months in one as such.

This is how it happened. My connection with the agricultural interest and with the backbone of the country was so slight, that when the teacher was explaining how much we owed the farmers of Ireland and asked me where our food came from, I replied, 'Summerhill', and when that strapping Christian Brother moved towards me in a manner that behoved no good to Brendan Francis Aidan Behan, though I knew I had given the wrong answer, the only alternative that came readily to mind was 'Dorset Street'.

I had no relations on a farm, and was not personally acquainted with a single farmer. I approved of farmers, particularly from Tipperary or West Cork, because I had heard older people speaking of Dan Breen and Tom Barry:

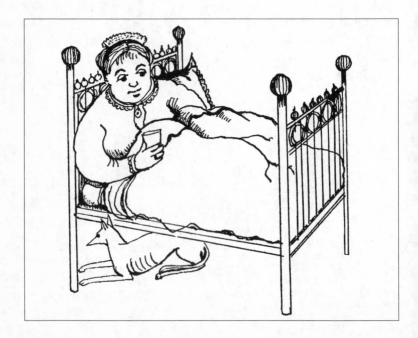

'They were shot in pairs
Coming up the stairs
By Sean Treacy and Dan Breen . . .'

Both of whom knew how to handle the Black and Tans. Anyhow up to quite an advanced age I did not know they used real horses at the races. I thought it was all done with telephones.

But I had never heard of the Anglo-Irish. I knew there were Protestants, because I played with half a dozen of them. I knew there were Jews, because I knew some and they had a cemetery in Fairview, and I thought they were a pretty daft lot because they had the date '5683' written on the stone over the door, though one of them from our way did write 'Did Your Mother Come From Ireland'. But that was later than the time I was in the castle.

Well, who let me into the castle? It was this way. A relation of mine was a young chap in the cattle trade. He was as good a judge of a beast as you'd get from here to Mulhuddart, though he was born round the North Circular Road, the same as the rest of us, and learned all he knew up in Prussia Street, working for a salesmaster.

There was this castle out in the County Dublin, and the people that owned it left it for a bit, because they got nervous during the Civil War.

But the place, from being left empty, was being ruined from damp and going to rack and ruin and all to that effect, and the people who owned it wrote from Margate or Miami, or wherever they were, and asked the salesmaster would he get someone to go and live in it for a bit.

To cut the long story short, our Richie, the young cattle fellow, said he didn't mind and out he went.

The next thing was, of a Sunday, my Granny and two of her sisters went out on a visit to see how he was getting on, and my granny said the air was a very good thing out there and would do all the good in the world to her other poor sister, Henrietta.

Poor Henrietta caught a bad cold at Parnell's funeral and hadn't been expected to live this forty year. She was only able to lie in bed and moan, 'Is any of yous ever going to make the drain of tea?'

When the teacup was not actually at her lips, she was bemoaning the fact that she was a 'poo—er orpher-a-n'. I ran out of the *Phantom of the Opera* because Lon Chaney put me in mind of her.

It was decided that the bit of air would do me good too and I joined the merry house-party, but damned nearly passed out because they gave me a room to myself. I was eventually brought in with my granny, for I didn't think much of this solitary-confinement act.

Our team was playing in the final of the Conway Cup in the Fifteen Acres, and the boys decided this was good for collective training. So they came out too, bringing with them a gramophone and a record with two sides to it, 'On Mother Kelly's Doorstep' and 'Gee, oh Gosh, oh Golly, I'm in love with Molly'. And a fellow called 'Thirsty' that trained greyhounds.

My Aunt Henrietta sat in the window over a field at the back to watch the team practising, and would shout dog's abuse at the players if everything wasn't going to her liking. Thirsty said they wouldn't mind him keeping the dogs in the drawingroom for a while. The kennels were leaking at home and it wasn't doing them any good.

Our Richie said the place was a cross between a sports' ground, a sanatorium and a relief scheme, and he was fit for the puzzle factory, and they said he could go on up there; they'd look after the castle till he came out.

We had a dance on a Sunday night. There were a lot of girls working in factories at that time, and they used to bring out cigarettes and sandwiches and cake for the team, and after tea there was dancing to the record, one side after the other, turn about being fair play.

Everything went like a canal boat up a hill till this Sunday night Richie came up, all white and pale, like someone on a weekend pass out of Glasnevin.

'You must have got a bad result,' said Thirsty.

'I'll be put up in the Joy,' moaned Richie.

'It was the Gorman yesterday,' said our outside-left. 'But a change is as good as a rest and it'll be nearer your work.'

'They're coming up the drive. Right now.'

So they were; the people that owned the place.

'Quick,' said the outside-left, 'out in the grounds the lot of yous.'

'Someone of yous wait here and give me a hand with me aunt.'

She was asleep, for once in a way, and they dumped her in a closet and left her there. The others went out with the footballers.

'I only hope them this-and-that dogs keeps easy,' muttered Richie to himself.

'I hope so and all,' said I.

'Oh, I'd forgotten you. What am I going to do with you?'

'I know,' said I. 'I can get under the dead dog in the front room.'

'That's not a dead dog, it's a dead tiger; but go on, get under it, only hurry.'

I did and only in time, for the next thing I heard the door open and this old one, and an old fellow, speaking to Richie.

They weren't gone very far when I heard a long and deep moaning.

'Cedric,' said the old one, very shiveringly, 'did you hear that? It's the banshee.'

But it wasn't. Only Thirsty's old bitch. She moaned again.

'Don't you think we'd s-s-see it better by daylight, C-Cedric?'

Cedric said nothing, but the next thing my Aunt Henrietta woke in her closet and moaned out through the door: 'Is any a yous ever going to make the dr-a-in a te-a-a? Sure, I'm only a poo-er . . .'

But the old one let a screech out of her and ran for the door and down the gravel path, leading Cedric by a short head.

What did I do? Just lay under the tiger, that's all. My Aunt Henrietta would scare you, even if you were used to her. You should have heard her!

Irish Press 23 October 1954

Even the English don't like it—how sorry they are to return

Nobody enters or re-enters England with greater reluctance than the intellectual native of that country. Howard and Monica went down the gangplank at Newhaven like early Christian martyrs. People have gone into Mountjoy with less reluctance.

For the matter of that, the intelligentsia of all countries is notoriously lacking in that sort of fervour that shows itself in frantic devouring of the old sod, to see if it tastes the same as it did on the way out.

Howard is a higher civil servant, and had finished a tour of British military establishments in various parts of the Continent. His wife went with him to keep him company and for the sake of the holiday.

We began a conversation on the way over from France. They asked me whether I intended to stay in England for long, and I told them I'd be there a couple of months. Monica wished to know if I knew it well. I said I knew a few places extremely well, without specifying what places.

Monica wanted to know if I liked living in England and watching with mounting distaste the white cliffs looming on the horizon, I did not like, for politeness' sake, to give her a straight answer. I said I thought my trip would be interesting.

But I need not have bothered. They both seemed to think that anyone of his own free will, leaving the Continent for England, must be more than a little mad.

After that we went down like a dinner with one another, and exchanged such pieces of cultural information as the story about the last words of Gertrude Stein, who sat up on her death-bed a couple of minutes before she died, and asked, 'What is the answer?' A second or two later she enquired, 'But what is the question?'

'Ah'd say she knows be this time,' said an Irish voice behind me. It was one of a band of students from Belfast I had met on the way over.

I left my northern brother giving grim consideration to these matters and went through the Customs with my friends.

For all they looted and robbed, the English made considerably less use of the swag than smaller imperialisms. The ugliness of most of London is unbelievable.

I was surprised to pass Piccadilly without noticing it, and Marble Arch is only about the same size as the Boer War memorial (known as 'Traitors' Gate') that they put up in place of Wolfe Tone's monument at Stephen's Green.

It is the second biggest suburb in the world, coming in length and breadth of built-up area considerably behind Los Angeles, which I am told extends for a hundred miles.

In the sense that I understand the word, the 'city' does not extend beyond the West End. A mile in any direction outside that, and so far as entertainment is concerned, at eleven o'clock at night you might as well be in Drimnagh or Ballygomartin.

Its people are kindlier, nosier and more respectable than any I have ever met.

The famed British reserve is as much a myth as the idea of the broth-of-a-boy Irishman, he of the ready wit and the warm heart and the great love for a fight.

Try it on the landlord or the grocer sometime. Tell him you'll give two rounds of the shillelagh in place of whatever you owe him and wait for the witty answer.

The landlord over here will know all about you if you remain with him for more than two days. And if it's a landlady she'll want to know more than that in twenty-four hours.

They also have an idea that most Irishmen go out in the morning and travel long distances by Tube to dig ditches for Lord Wimpey and Earl MacAlpine.

I was wakened at six o'clock on two occasions 'to go to work'. Luckily my accent, which I just discovered is as much of a 'brogue' as Barry Fitzgerald's, made unintelligible most of the flow of language with which the poor old one was greeted in the brightening morn.

Always I was met with the enquiry as to what I was. This was not meant in the Six Counties sense of Fenians or Orangemen, which political or religious curiosity I am beginning to think is not the most troublesome kind.

What the landlady wanted to know was what was I in terms of the industrial effort.

I thought of saying I was a progress-chaser or a Power Samas operator, both of which occupations I have seen mentioned in the newspaper advertising columns. But for both these occupations one must have false teeth and a taste for sausage rolls, so I said I was interested in cattle.

She made further enquiry as to what part of the cattle business I was interested in and I answered: 'Oh, steak, silverside, corned beef, brains, liver, heart, any part as you might say, though I have never tried the nostrils. That, madam, I am bound to admit.'

I am writing this in Bayswater, which is quite a pleasant mid-Victorian suburb, one of the residential areas of the great manufacturing bourgeoisie and now famous for its murders.

Mr Christie had his private morgue just up the road in Notting Hill; Flying Officer Heath's strangularium was across the way in Gloucester Road. And the sink down which Haigh poured numerous of his acquaintances is in a kitchen round the corner.

The day is dark and grey, though brightened by a memory of the wise and smiling south, like a flash of sun, a reminder of the summer.

In Westbourne Grove, outside Lawrence's Store, he stood. A stout little Italian, with a figure that owed nothing to privation throwing out from the roots of him, and rising over the basses of his own accordion, his splendid tenor voice: '*Ave Maria . . . gratia plena.*'

O craft, thy name is Luigi! The strong West of Ireland faces and the softer, smoother looks of French and Italian smiled into one another, and navvies and waitresses, barbers and busmen, Cork and Calabria, remembered their mothers' people, it being Saturday and they out on the holiday promenade, and rewarded Luigi well for reminding them of it.

I meet the hyphenated Irishmen

I come from one of the few parts of Ireland with no tradition of emigration. I knew a family on our street whose widowed mother knocked it out for seven of them by selling apples and 'Half-Time Jimmies' at football matches. The eldest boy assisted at All-Ireland finals with the teams' colours decorated at that time with 'Come on, Kerry,' and photographs of the immortal Sheehy, or the black and amber and Lory Meagher's head.

They thought as little of distance as they did of the foreign games controversy, and would cross over to Liverpool for the big match with as little difficulty as they would go up to Dalymount or over to Shelbourne Park.

The pram of apples and chocolates was to be found as often outside Goodison Park as outside 'Croker'. Half the district went over to Liverpool for the laying of the foundation stone of the new cathedral, so I shouldn't say we were totally untravelled but, until comparatively recently, I never heard of anyone going to work in England and no-one seemed to go to America.

A man in Ballinasloe said to me one time that the reason was that we wouldn't be let in.

For some reason, however, the idea of hyphenated Irishmen never interested us very much. An Irishman, to us, was someone, Catholic, Protestant or Jew, born in Ireland, and we could not very well understand why any other should claim or wish to claim the description.

Neither did 'O'Donnell Abu' ever strike me as the sort of song one raved over to the tune of an almost endless number of rapturously received encores.

These reflections are prompted by a morning's vocal exercise I've had in Danny Meehan's Irish hostelry in King's Cross where Tinny MacPhail, a Glasgow son of Scots-Irish parents, and an O'Donnell on his mother's side, made me sing the maternal clan anthem often enough for him to pick it up.

Now he is well equipped to send the war cry arising on the gale, forty or fifty times over himself.

Not that the Glasgow Irish do not have their own songs. Besides the lament for Johnny Thompson, Celtic goalie killed on the football field in 1934, they sing, almost as a national anthem, the song of the 'Smashing of the Van', about the attempt to rescue Frank Carty in the Tan time.

'. . . they arrested Father MacRory,
a Catholic clergyman,
But they only showed their own ignorance,
At the smashing of the van.'

And there are also the local hyphenated Irish.

Like most people I have seen reports in the papers of more or less inoffensive citizens being battered unconscious by Teddy Boys, teenaged boys whose uniform is an elaborate imitation of what a well-dressed man was wearing in the days of Edward the Seventh: drainpipe trousers, long jacket with velvet collar, and what my father would call an All-For-Ireland-League MP's overcoat.

The other night, I was standing at a coffee stall, nourishing myself with a cup of tea and a sandwich, watching half a dozen of these gentry devouring jellied eels.

By the same token, I am a great believer in sampling the local delicacies anywhere I may happen to be, but I draw a firm line at jellied eels. I understand from an article by Mr Benedict Kiely in this newspaper that they come from the burns and glens of County Antrim and that numerous canty bodies make a wheen of ha'pence on the export trade, from Toomsbridge to Waterloo Bridge.

I will take his word for it that jellied eels are wholesome fare for man and beast, and leave it at that.

Anyway, I was at this stall at about one in the morning, and these Teddy Boys seemed to be giving me searching looks. I am not notoriously a nervous type, and was not reared in such a sheltered atmosphere as to feel I was slumming by going down the East End.

But I was a long way from barracks, and while I was not less than twice the weight of any two of these anti-Parnellites, I did not feel in the humour for taking on six of them.

Besides, the world and Garrett Reilly has learned from Sunday reading that the least offensive of the Edwardian armoury includes a bicycle chain and a blunt instrument fashioned from the strap-hanging equipment of the London Passenger Transport Board.

The most velvety Teddy Boy looked over at me and said: 'Eye.'

'Eye,' said I, learning the language apace.

'Yew Ahrish?'

I admitted as much, and wondered which of them I could drop before the belt on the back of the head. I could see the headstone, in the 'Nevin, if they ever gathered up the bits and sent them home: '*Breandáin Ó Beacháin, coshálta chun báis ar Dhroichead Waterloo, 1954. His memory is a lesson to us all*' . . . to keep away from jellied eel fanciers.

He turned to his friends and said: 'Vere. Woh eye sye?'

He smiled at me, and said: 'These geezers contradicted me. I knew you was Ahrish w'en I 'eard your browgue. We're all Ahrish 'ere.'

Proudly he pointed out his friends: ' 'e's Mac Carfy, en 'e's O'Leary, en 'Ealy, en 'Ogan, en Kelly, en my name is — give a guess.'

'Murphy.'

'That's it,' said he, delightedly, 'and my mum is a Flanagan.'

'Gentlemen,' said I, 'I'm really pleased to hear this,' and raised my cup in a salute.

A young lady employee of the Irish Government here works for a Catholic Youth organisation, and told me of a dance they ran which was visited by Cardinal Griffin.

The archiepiscopal party beamed on the young dancers, who pranced around sedately till they left, and then went into the wildest and liveliest sort of jiving.

My friend commented on this to one of them, and on the rapidity with which they accelerated the pace of the light fantastic once the visitors were gone.

'Well?' asked the lad quite indignantly, 'what did you expect us to do? Be-bop in front of an archbishop? What do you take us for, 'Eathens?'

Irish Press 20 November 1954

So many notabilities have talked of these LANE pictures

Now, autumn leaves are falling,
The light is growing dim,
The painter wipes his pot clean down,
And throws his brushes in . . .

Or, as the saying has it, 'cover me up till the first of March.' That was the kind of saying I was forced to put up with, and I a painter's apprentice in this city. Though, in reply, I could remark that putty and paint made the carpenter a saint.

Howsome-ever, as the man said, first carefully removing his butt from his lower lip, I was not all that good of an apprentice. Though not devoid of ambition in the graining, lettering and marbling line, it was agreed that my talents lay in the placing of dockets, and running out for the charge-hand's curer of a Saturday morning.

My mathematics played me false the day Workman won the National for, acting on information received from a little matchmakeress who got it in the factory of its owner, I switched all bets on to the winner, including alas, heavy place-bets on Kilstar and Saint George, which paid fantastic prices, even at one-fourth the odds, so 'twas little enough I made for my trouble.

My father and grandfathers were painters, and at an exhibition of Patrick Swift's, Victor Waddington remarked that of all present, my father was the only painter with a union card.

My granny was a forewoman gilder in Brindley's of Eustace Street, and on my mother's side the Kearneys were, and are, similarly engaged.

For all that, mayhap because of that, I am allergic to painting. Not to paint, mark you. But to putting the stuff on. (Grim chorus of assent from walking foremen and chargers, from Dublin, Cork City, Youghal, Belfast and Donaghadee: 'You don't have to tell *us*.')

I even like looking at a job well done, and have been known, in the middle of Debussy's *Peléas et Mélisande*, to force the attentions of

[54]

Messrs John Ryan and Frederick May, who had the good fortune to be sitting on either side of me (otherwise they might have missed it), to a rather neat bit of repair filling on the Gaiety ceiling.

And in company with another military refugee from the trade, Mr Joseph Tomelty, I commented adversely on the papering of a night-club in Villiers Street, London. Joe and I agreed that it was 'lapped' where, in an establishment with any pretence to decency, it should have been 'butted'. Which drew from the cynical lip of Mr Con O'Leary, the comment that in a new town, the first thing a tinker looks at is his horse.

Strangely, there are few house-painter painters, picture painters, I mean. Few *peintres en batiment* become *artistes peintres*.

I can think of only one famous modern painter, who began by painting houses: Georges Braque. Though for that matter Monsieur Braque was also, in his day, a professional boxer.

There have been firemen artists, Grandma Moses, peasant artists by the acre, priest artists, child artists, and there are people who claim that the famous English artist, Sir Winston Churchill, is an author.

For the matter of that, there are not wanting those who make out that his colleague, Sir Alfred Munnings, is a horse. But seldom do you ever hear of a house-painter artist.

I remember once there was a fisherman artist, and his work was hung in very august surroundings, and big ha-ha in the papers about him being an uninstructed simple man, and all to that effect, and at the opening of the exhibition old ones from the cultural areas of the six and seven and nine and ten bus routes were all gabbing around this chap, who had cleaned off the herring leavings for the day and stood, rather more stylishly dressed than the ordinary artist artists, modestly giving his opinions on life and art.

Then the door burst open and a very well-known Irish artist stood there, his massive frame adorned in the habilaments of a trawlerman. Enormous seaboots, a blue woollen jersey, sou'wester, and rubbers he wore, and trailed from his shoulder was about twenty yards of tram net.

The first to recover from this apparition was the then chief among artists, an old man of ancient lineage, who directed a stern and indignant inquiry towards the figure in the doorway.

'Sir, what is the meaning of appearing amongst your friends and brothers in this preposterous costume?'

From the doorway came the drawled reply: 'Oh, I thought you knew. *I*—with a nonchalant shrug of his net-draped shoulder, in the direction of the serge-suited fisherman artist—'*I* am an artist fisherman.'

I could give as glib a bit of guff about 'tactile values' and the 'melodic line' as the next but it is not from any expert knowledge of painting that I write of the Lane Pictures. It just happens that they are as much my property as yours, or Montgomery Hyde's or any other Irishman's.

And I have *seen* them, or some of them. Besides the Corot, Renoir, Manet, Degas and Pisarro pictures, there are a couple I wouldn't sentence my worst enemy to look at, and then only for a laugh.

There's one bit of Victorian anecdotage called 'The Mountebank', showing a poor showman lying on the grass in a country lane, with his faithful dog and horse.

Its only interest for Lane would have been the Irish origin of the painter, John Lewis Brown. He was born, reared, and died in France, and was patronised by Napoleon III. His work shows every sign of it. This one is not exhibited.

Montgomery Hyde's name goes down to history with the very interesting list of those who fought for the return of the Lane Pictures, including the Countess Markiewicz, Dr Thomas Bodkin, Oliver St John Gogarty, Lady Gregory, Jim Larkin, Major Brian Cooper, Dermod O'Brien, Sean O'Casey, Eamon de Valera, W. B. Yeats and Sarah Purser.

On the other side may be mentioned the name, scarcely remembered in any other connection, of Lord Duveen, who gave a new wing to the Tate Gallery on condition that they held on to the Lane pictures. The building, incidentally, was given 'to the British nation as a thanksgiving for peace'.

Most prominent of those who caused the trouble in the first place, by refusing a proper home in Dublin for the pictures, was the late Mr

William Martin Murphy. It seems that his constant concern for the welfare of the Dublin working class overcame his aesthetic inclinations.

He thought that while slum conditions were as they were they should build no new art galleries. Furthermore, he said in a letter to his own *Irish Independent*: 'I believe the Lord Mayor is mistaken or misled if he thinks there is any burning desire on the part of the ratepayers of Dublin to contribute £25,000 towards a memorial to Sir Hugh Lane, in order to house a few pictures.'

One of the pictures I saw was Renoir's 'Les Parapluies'—some people caught in a shower of rain, with umbrellas raised over them. A holiday crowd, perhaps, enjoying Sunday afternoon in the park, and including a little girl holding a hoop.

But you might as well hope to know the blue of the sky from a wireless commentary, as gauge my idea of this picture, from a description of it.

Its effect on me was like the first hearing of Beethoven's Fifth Symphony on Hector Berlioz, who said: 'Leaving the hall, after the orchestra had finished, I could not find my head to get my hat on.'

Irish Press 20 November 1954

Behind him Lester Pigott left trails of havoc

'Brending Behing.'
 'Mrs Brennan.'
 'How's Londing?'
 'Who?'
 'Londing. Didn't you come home from the Contingnent be Lond-ing?'
 'That's right.'
 'Well, *came meal a vault yeh.*'
 'What me?'
 'There's the Irishman for yous. *Came meal a vault yeh*—A hundred, thousand welcomes.'
 'Thank you, Mrs Brennan, that's more nor civil of you.'
 'I'd a thought anyone would have known what "*came meal a vault yeh*" meant. Usen't it to be written up over the stage in the Queen's. Isn't that right, Mr Cripping?'
 Crippen lifted his head from the unvarnished half of a pint tumbler and nodded, gloomily.
 'That's right. "*Céad míle fáilte*, kindly remember you're not at home and do not spit; nor pass out tickets after the second interval; orange-sucking prohibited during cornet solo." But don't talk to me about London.'
 'Ah,' said Mrs Brennan, feelingly, 'poor ould Crip, he's like that since the other day at the Curragh. Lester Piggott let him down for a three cross-double and the same back, anything to come first fav. at the other meeting.'
 'Thanks be to God,' said Crippen, 'he doesn't come over more oftener. The short while he was here he done more damage than Cromwell or Willie Nevett. I'd *him* at the end of a length of accumu-lators the size of a summans in the Irish Two Thousand, and he let me down for one pound one and three (less tax).'
 'Ah, sure, Mr Cripping, that's months ago. It's no use keeping up a thing like that for ever,' said Mrs Brennan. 'Better to forget it.'

'I can never forget it, and me with three pounds eighteen and three-pence, less tax, going on to a two-to-one shot.'

'We keep the past for pride,' said I.

'Oh, he's like that this week past,' said Mrs Brennan, 'and if you had seen him in the shop when the result came in he was like a raging deming. Going round looking at the sheets and muttering, "Omagh, Armagh, Armagh, Omagh," like an incantating charm or smell, like what you're warned against in the Cathechissing. I don't think it's lucky.

'Still, Mr Cripping, sup up, you're in your granny's and don't make strange. In honour of Mr Brending Behing's safe return to his native vegigibble market. Concepta!'

An ancient, indestructible countenance, wrinkled and rugged enough to contain a shower of rain, but at present holding no more than the faintest traces of previous repasts of snuff, upturned itself from the inside of a shawl. 'Mrs Jewel and darling, did I hear you say something?'

'I've to go and watch me grandchild's eldest, the Lotty one, get a couple of skips of fruit over to me pitch, the butt-end of Moore Street. You know the pitch poor ould Funny Noises willed me?'

''Deed I do, the Lord have mercy on her, a good poor soul, poor ould Funny Noises. Still, she couldn't take her bit of Moore Street with her.'

'Still, and all, it was decent of her, and I looking for a bit of ground for me descendings. You might as well have a half in respect of her, not to mind Brending Behing being home, Me-Hall!'

'Yes, Mrs Brennan, ma'am,' said Michael.

'Two pints of stout for the menkinds, and us ladies will have two half-ones and a bottle of Johnny-jump up.' She turned to me. 'A surjing gave me the tip. Lovely man, he was. Only for the ould drop. Too fond of it.

'Man sent up to be operated on for an ingrowing toenail. Me poor surjing read the card wrong and thought it was a head amputating was required. Amputated the head, God love him, very severe operating, the patiengt never come out of it and the poor surjing was dis-

[59]

graced for life.'

'I knew one of them Swaines up in George's Packet, had his thumb amputated.'

'I remember them,' said Mrs Brennan, 'they were married into the Leadbeaters.'

'That's right,' said Crippen, cheering himself up with a pull on his pint. 'Well, they were in a kind of religion that was very conscientious about the last day, and about getting up out of the grave, the way you were in this world. Well, Apollo Swaine . . .'

'Apollo?' I enquired.

'Yes, he got that name from hawking refreshments and shouting at the football matches, "Cigarettes, chocolate, toffee-app-oll-oh." Well, anyway, when he came out of the hospital he brought the thumb with him and gave a kind of a little wake for it in Jimmy-the-Sports' bar up on our corner.

'Had it on the counter beside him, bringing it up to bury it. "I'm going to put it where the rest of me will be when I die," says Apollo. "A fellow would look well on the last day, running round the Nevin like a half-thick and asking everyone, and they gathering up their ould traps themselves, "Ech, did you see e'er a sign of a thumb knocking round?"

'So we all agreed that there was a deal in what he said, and he invited us to the funeral of his thumb. We got up to the Nevin and buried it, and some was crying when the thumb was covered up in the ground, but Apollo mastered himself and gave a bar of a song before saying farewell.

'I can hear him this minute, and we all joined in with him when he sung out to his poor ould thumb, "And you will sleep in peace until I come to thee."'

'Still, it wasn't like having a head amputating, having a tum amputating,' said Mrs Brennan. 'When all is said and done, a body does have two tums.'

Irish Press 4 December 1954

He was once Crippen the piper

'In the British Milisha he was, my poor fellow, wasn't he, Maria Concepta? And a fine man, too,' said Mrs Brennan.

'He was all that,' said Maria Concepta, 'and I heard my own fellow saying that your fellow was as safe as houses in the war. He only had to put on his busby and march away. The Boers thought it was a hedgehog moving.'

'But all the same, I was thrilled to bits waiting for him to finish his month's training on the Curragh. I was faithful to him the whole four weeks and when the dread millingterry word of command rang out, and the period of separashing was over, and the sergeant-major roars, "Milisha to your work-houses, poor-houses, dosshouses and jails, disperse!" there I was, standing behind him, waiting to pick him up as he fell out. To pick him up and carry him home.'

'Aye, indeed,' said Maria Concepta. 'A tough little man he was, too, like the day he punched the countryman in the ankle for asking him whether he was a child or a midget.'

'Were you ever in the Army, Mister Cripping, sir?'

Crippen gave a mirthless laugh.

'Was I ever what? Are you codding me or what? Are you getting it up for me or what? Was I ever in the Army? Did you ever hear of the Malpas Street ambush? Did you ever hear of the attack on O'Keefe's the knacker's? Did you ever hear of the assault on the Soap Works in Brunswick Street? Or the raid on the Sloblands? Did yous?' He glared at me. 'Well, God almighty, that's the Irish all over. Did *you* ever hear tell of the dead who died for Ireland? Well, you're looking at one of them.'

'I'm sorry for your trouble,' I muttered, for want of something to say.

'I suppose yous never heard of the pitched battle at the Back of the Pipes? And I suppose, talking about pipes, yous never heard of the lone piper who played at the massacre of Mullinahack? There was a song written about it.

'I was not long learning the pipes. But now yous know it, I don't mind telling yous that my nickname in the old Seventh Batt. was the Cock of the North.

'That was really on account of me mother keeping the poultry above in Phibsboro. Ah, when I think of the old days . . .' He sighed, looking into the depths of his tumbler.

'I was through the whole lot. The Tan War, the Civil War, the Economic War.'

'Ah, more luck to you,' said Maria Concepta. 'Didn't I sing for the boys?'

'You sang?' I asked.

'She did, Brending Behing. If you heard her singing "Home to Our Mountings" you'd know all about it,' said Mrs Brennan.

'I don't doubt you,' said I.

'That woman,' said Crippen, pointing to Maria Concepta, 'was principal soprano in the Hammond Lane.'

'That's right,' said Mrs Brennan, 'in the Hammongd Laying Fouingdry Choir.'

'I suppose,' said I, with a weak grin, 'yous put on the opera *The Rose of Castile.* Have you me? *The Rows of Cast Steel.* It's a joke,' I pleaded, 'from a book by a man by the name of James Joyce.'

'Do you think,' said Crippen severely, 'we're all thicks and idiots here? Certainly we heard of James Joyce, the man who wrote *Useless*. I was in the inntellimigentzia. . .'

I'd forgotten Crippen's connection with the world of letters. He had knowledge of a bookie who took stamped addressed envelopes and International Reply Coupons to the odds and ran to this bookie regular errands for both members of the staff of a cultured quarterly, since deceased.

'Be the way, what happened your gills?'

'The former assistant editor?'

'Of course. D'you think I was enquiring about the charwoman?'

'He's still with the BBC.'

'I wonder, Mr Cripping, if you'd ever give me youngest grandchild's eldest a bit of a note to him? He's the next one of me descendings to leave school and at the moment he seems fit for nothing but to be this year's net-ball champying. He's made to be an enjing-driver, and if your friend in the CIE could—'

'It's not the CIE,' said Crippen, 'it's the BBC.'

'I beg your parding, Mr Cripping.'

'Give us that bit offa song you sang in the Trouble,' said Crippen in the direction of Maria Concepta.

'I might as well. Wait till I clear me throat.'

A sound as of the death-rattle came from under her shawl and then, without further warning, a most blood-curdling moan went through the shop, as she threw back her covering and bayed to the ceiling. 'Howl, howl, *howl* . . .'

The cat glanced anxiously round and at the third note got down from the window and ran out the door.

'You never lost it,' said Crippen, nodding his head in appreciation.

Maria Concepta screwed up her face another bit, and went on 'Howl! How long will dear old Ireland be unfree?'

'Lovely,' muttered Mrs Brennan, rapping on the counter, and humming to herself. 'Oh, never marry a soldier, an airman or a maree-ing, if you can get a rebel in his uniform of greeing . . .'

Irish Press 11 December 1954

Let's go on a pupil's tour of the nation via the Tolka

The Coombe crowd are hot stuff. Never mind your *Dublin Opinion* jokes about Corkmen and Northerners. The Liberty boys would give them a run for their money any day of the week. No need for them to go into the Civil Service or this *teóranta* or that *teóranta*, or into the newspaper offices for the matter of that, to get a crust and a sup of tay.

If you ever bought a 'sticka taffy' or a 'bara jocklit', at the Curragh or Leopardstown, it's money on that it emanated from Blackpitts, or thereabouts, and the 'hang sangwich' you nourished yourself with at Baldoyle more than likely had its origins in the *haute cuisine*, not of France, but of Francis Street.

I'll admit that in the palmy days of our adolescence, this kind of Coombe-olatry would, in my native Monto, have been regarded as dangerously near treachery to the Northside. Spike wouldn't have liked it.

But, since the times of the amphibian battle of Tolka Park, the day of the combined land and water operation and the Kevin Street Commando, a lot of water has gone down the Tolka, too much, perhaps.

And, anyway, we're all that mixed up in the last twenty years of new housing that, as the woman said in the Flats:

'You never know what kind you're going to have beside you.'

She had just discovered that her next door neighbour was *his* mother.

I'll get back to the Coombe in a minute but, it just occurred to me, there's no song about the Tolka.

And as the man said, if it wasn't much of a river, it was the best we had. Brian Boru's son was drowned in it, and it's not every river you could say that about.

Seán Russell littered Annesley Bridge with dead ones in Easter Week. Go on, Behan, your blood's in your knuckles.

On the other hand, it is said that a Dublin Fusilier *in extremis* on the battlefields of Flanders, when offered a drink of water, shook his head, and told them to bring it home and give it to the Tolka, which needed it more.

The only reason I can think of as to why there should be no song about the Tolka, is the impossibility of rhyming 'Tolka' with anything else but 'polka'.

Not that there are many songs about the Liffey, or the city itself, for the matter of that.

There have been *ersatz* efforts like the following by Lady Caterwaul, or some such name, that wouldn't go away and leave the people die in peace the time of the cholera:

Oh Bay of Dubling,
My heart you're trubbling,
Like frozen fountaings—
More power to you, Mrs Brenning ma'am; your blood's worth bottling.
—*The sunbeam's bubbling. . .*
There's nothing like the Belfast mill songs:
You'll be sure to know a doffer,
When she goes down the town,
With her shawl and her clogs,
And her hair hanging down . . .
I don't suppose they're the correct words. But it's a real song though geographically more of the Irish school of canty bodies. And certainly nothing to equal the beautiful songs of Cork City, which do not receive their just due, any more than anything else barring Joe Lynch, from that delightful land of pig meat and porter. Probably because they never did anything on us.

'You're getting very fond of the Corkone-yeeings, in your old age, Brending Being.'

'Ah, sure, maybe its only to spite the other crowd, Mrs Brenning, ma'am.'

I do not mean 'The Banks of My Own Lovely Lee', though I know every word of it, and have, before now, reduced audiences to tears by the bucketful with my rendering of it; nor do I mean even the more genuine and stirring airs of West Cork:

'From east to west, from north to south,
They tried to hunt the column out,

Till a muster at Rosscarbery's rout,
Awoke them from their dreaming.
Come, piper, play a martial air,
For the gallant boys who conquered there,
A merry tune to banish care, not mournful,
Nor solemn,
But the grandest tune that was ever played
By the fighting squad of the Third Brigade,
Whose glorious deeds, shall never fade,
The boys of Barry's column . . .'

'This is like a Curse Umper Errin tour of the coumtry, Brending Being; when are we getting back to the Coombe?'

Next week, good people, via Timahoe Bog.

Irish Press 18 December 1954

Those days of *The Growler*

'Listen,' said Michael this morning, looking at Crippen, 'all these ambushes at Malpas Street and Mullinahack and the raid on the Sloblands that you were talking about. How is it I never heard of them, nor no one else?'

'How is it you never heard of them?' asked Crippen, 'because they were done in secret, that's why.'

'I didn't live too far away from Malpas Street, and I never heard as much as a shot from it.'

'We used silencers,' said Crippen, 'silencers—' he looked ominously around the shop— 'and knives. As the poem said—'

'Oh, I love a poem,' said Mrs Brennan. 'I learned one meself, once, be Mangle.'

'Be who?'

'Be Mangle. James Claryawance Mangle. I learned it at school. "Soloming. Where is thy Trowing? It is gone in the wie-ingd. Babyling! Where is thy might? It is gone in the wieingd, and all . . ."'

'This poem I was talking about,' said Crippen, 'was printed in a secret paper called *The Growler*, and it was signed "Seville Place". We all had to use Irish place names. One fellow was "Shanganagh", another was "Slivenamon", and I was "Seville Place". Yes I might as well admit it, I was "Seville Place", the whole time, and yous never knew, now did yous?' He looked at me.

'I hadn't an idea,' said I.

'Well, you know now,' said Crippen. 'Me secret's out. But what harm, we're all friends here. You might as well hear it, anyway.' He set his face towards the door and began:

'Twas next winter, last summer, the year before last,
And a man with a hammer sat breaking his fast,
To hell with Lloyd George, and he let out a roar,
For Ireland beats England by six goals to four . . .'

'That's a deep bit of a poem, I can tell yous. A deep meaning in every other word of it.'

'I've no doubt,' said I.

'Ah, sure the world and Garret Reilly knows, Mr Cripping, that you're putrid from educayshing.'

'Well, I can tell you what Lloyd George, himself, said at the time about me poem. In the British House of Commons—'

'The Brishish House of Commings,' said Mrs Brennan, 'let yous all mark that.'

'He said, "if I knew the misacrint that goes be the name of "Seville Place", and wrote that poem in the dirty Sinn Féin rag, *The Growler*, I'd give him, jeering and jibeing and making little of people. I'd cut the two hands off him, and leave him, that he wouldn't be able to pick a one and one much less write poems." ' (Irish Nat. interjections of 'Mitchelstown'. Cheers from Gov. benches). 'It's all in an old paper I have at home.'

'You done your bit all right,' said Maria Concepta.

'Oh, sure Wolve Towing was only in the ha'penny place to Mr Cripping. And he never feared debt.'

'Death?' said Crippen, with a scornful laugh. 'I was used to that a long time ago. Like the time I lost the coffin.'

'Lost a coffing, Mr Cripping?'

'That's right, ma'm. I was living out be Cloghran at the time, taking the country air for meself, on account of some lead disappearing off a roof, and badminded people . . .'

'Bad luck to them,' said Maria Concepta, 'don't mind them, Sir.'

'No, just tell us about the coffing.'

'I was coming from Cloghran into Dorset Street for a few messages and a man be the name of Jowls Hanratty come up and told me his old father was dead, and would I bring out a coffin on the back of the pony and cart.

'I said I would, and he said just to get stock size and brass handles, and off I went.

'On the way back it started to snow, and I'd been into a few places to warm meself up, and was nearly home when I looked around and the coffin was gone.

'I walked back and searched the road as best I could, when a peeler comes up. "What are you doing round here this hour of the night?" said he. "I'm after losing a coffin," said I. "I'll give you coffin," said he, "if you don't move on out of that." So I had to take an hour explaining to him that I really had lost it.

"'Oh, it's genuine all right, constable," said I. "I'm after losing a coffin, and I wouldn't mind, constable, but it's not my own."'

'You'd feel awful, right enough, and maybe it's what people would think you were after doing away with it, the same as you did with the lead off of the roof,' said Maria Concepta, finishing in some confusion, when she felt Mrs Brennan's indignant eye on her.

'I hope you're not instiganayshing that Mr Cripping is a teef?'

To cause a diversion, I asked them what they were having.

Irish Press 1 January 1955

Remember Duck-the-Bullet

'Press,' said Mrs Brennan. We looked at her with a note of interrogation on each countenance; my own, Crippen's and Maria Concepta's. That is to say if you could describe the last-mentioned as a countenance.

'Press,' said Mrs Brennan, 'and dresser and chester-drawers and wardrobe, he'd leave them all in smithereens, and small-sized ones at that, when the fit came on him. Poor ould Duck-the-Bullet. It was really a kind of homesickness made him do it. Homesickness for the Somme in 1916.

'But be the time he'd finished with the furniture you wouldn't know the difference between the North Lotts and Flanders. And the drilling was the worst. His poor wife Esther Judas, Ace we called her for short, though she preferred Judy herself, and the daughter Nono, that was named in honour of *No, No, Nanette*, that was on in the Roto next door to the hospital when she was born, would have to get up in the middle of the night and stand there, while he charged them up and down the room with the sweeping-brush and showed them how to point and parry.'

'Well, I always say,' said Maria Concepta, saying it, 'that you can't beat a millingterry man for a husband. Always a bit of gas of some description. Me own poor fellow carried me three times around Mountjoy Square on a Sunday night in the summer of 'nought three, to show me how he rescued Lady Smith in the Boer War. You remember him, Mrs Brennan, ma'am?'

'Indeed and I do, Maria Concepta, and a fine presings of a man he was too. Wasn't he, Mr Cripping?'

'He was all that,' said Crippen. 'I heard said they were hard set to make out whether he was the biggest dwarf or the smallest giant in the whole of the Dublin Fusiliers.'

'Ah me,' moaned Maria Concepta, 'me dead hero. But go on, Mrs Brennan, ma'am, and tell us about poor ould Duck-the-Bullet. Him and my poor fellow joined up together, having been let outa the Joy the one morning.'

'When he was half sobered up then, he'd tell poor Ace, the wife, to cut off his head. "Here," he'd say, taking up the hatchet that he was chopping up the furniture with, "take that in your hand and say the words after me, and chop me head off. I must have got a bad half off of Dewlaps last night, and I'm too sick to wait for the market. Go on, Ace, cut off me head when I tell you."

'"Duck-the"—that's what she called him for short, a kind of pet name—"but I couldn't do the like of that. You'd be going around like Hanna Bow Lane with your head tucked under your arm."'

'Poor ould Duck-the Bullet, I used to love the way he'd rend the marching song,' said Maria Concepta. 'I heard it the day meself and me own fellow got married.

'I'll never forget in the sacristy, me a bride and the groom so fine and fierce-looking in his red tunic and blue trousers and waxed moustache, and the priest lifting him up to kiss me and his pals of the regiment outside and they singing the marching song, led be poor ould Duck-the-Bullet.'

A frightening noise, like the cry of an out-of-work banshee, came from the lips of Maria Concepta:

'Oh, with your left right, right about turn, this is the way we go,
Charging with fixed bayonets, the terror of every foe,
The glory of ould Ireland and a thousand buccaneers,
And a terror to creation were The Dublin Fusiliers . . .'
She finished on a sigh: 'Ah! If only he was here to hear me.'

'Ah sure he's better off,' said Mrs Brennan.

'You could say that again,' muttered Crippen.

Irish Press 10 February 1955

'I'm back from the Continong'

Like many a one since 1950 I'm apt to say, 'I've just got back from the Continong.' Well, I have and I can tell you one thing and that's not two, that the weather in most of France was every bit as bad as you had here. I arrived in Calais and stepped off the boat on to six inches of snow, and more coming down.

Like the cute old sleeveen that I am where anything connected with drinking and eating is concerned, I decided it would be better to buy a bottle of wine and some comestibles, and eat it in the carriage, rather than trust to what the hawkers might present us with at the stops en route.

For on the third class from Calais, at this time of the year, they have no restaurant on the train.

On the Blue Train, of course, you could look in the windows of the Pullman and see the rich settling down for a banquet of some hundreds of miles, and I've no doubt you could order anything from a

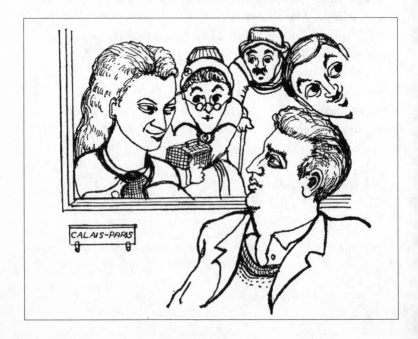

CALAIS-PARIS

[72]

live trout to a young child, if you fancied it and had the money to pay for it, or the money to go first class. But myself and my first wife were only on that route because we missed the Newhaven boat-train, which is cheaper and very comfortable.

I know Dieppe, Rouen and Dunkerque as well as I know Newry, Donaghadee or Drogheda, and Dieppe is a nice friendly place.

If you know how to do it you can dodge out under the train at the Gare Maritime—it's out in the street—and snake over to a wineshop and get cheese and *vin rouge*, and get back on the train again before you could say Lennox Robinson.

There used to be a wineshop owned by a Limerickman and called the BBC Wine Store.

They are very fond of third-class passengers in Dieppe, and at the height of the season the assmacrockery unloading the Rolls or the Daimler on the quay seem a little out of place, but Calais was not so well disposed towards the poor.

The town is so far from the quay that, setting off to look for my supplies, my first wife waved an almost tearful good-bye as I shuffled over the snowy wastes in my crêpe soles (thirty-two-and-six in Henry Street), looking like the late Rin-tin-tin going to do something very faithful. The town was too far away to get within an ass's bawl of a shop, so regretfully I trudged back after fifteen minutes in the blizzard.

But what a heartful welcome greeted me at the carriage window of my Calais-Paris express (via Amiens and Ville-cochon-sur-mer with a couple of dozen stops at intervening points to let old ones on with goats).

With what a heartfelt sigh of relief my first wife breathed down at me through the snow.

'Brendan, I thought you'd never come back.'

'*Oh, go raibh maith agat go deo, a ghrá, mar gheall ar an bhfáilte lách sin.*' I smiled, manlike. It may be that I owe that much that I have to go to Mass in a cab. What if I was unsuccessful in digging up some scoff for the trip?

Somebody anxious that I should come back. 'Your heart was in your mouth, thinking I'd be lost?'

'Well, you've got the tickets and the passports. I'd look well, I'm sure, left wandering round with no papers, looking for the price of a telephone call to the Irish Embassy from somewhere between Ameyens and Paris.'

'Amm-ee-ah.'

'What's that?'

'Amm-ee-ah. The place between here and Paris.'

'It's Ameyens. A-m-i-e-n-s.'

'Yes, but it is pronounced "Amm-ee-ah".'

'Listen, if we ever get home and thaw ourselves out in the Gulf Stream well enough to walk, just try walking up to a Guard in Talbot Street and ask him to direct you to Amm-ee-ah Street Station!'

However, in the heel of the hunt we got to the railway station of Saint Lazare.

In the course of the next few days I showed my wife the Opéra and the Louvre. She said when I said, 'See that, that's the Eiffel Tower,' that her sight, thanks be to God, was not so bad that she would be likely to miss the tallest object in Europe at a distance of ten yards.

In return, when we did get home and tottered off the B and I and got three-quarters way up the North Wall, she brought me round the corner of Store Street and pointed. 'See that?' she asked.

I said I did.

'Well,' said she, 'that's Amm-ee-ah Street Station.'

Irish Press 12 March 1955

The family was in the Rising

But who can talk of give and take,
What should be and what not
While those dead men are loitering there
To stir the boiling pot?
(W. B. Yeats: 'Sixteen Dead Men')

'To take as a headquarters the most prominent target in the whole city,' said a man in a middle-aged growl, 'what ridiculous strategy.'

Old George Roberts took the tumbler from his little full lips and stroked his beard. 'But what taste—what impeccable taste,' said he.

Me life on you, said I: for I knew what he meant. Hadn't I stood in the Queen's Theatre, with the frenzied Saturday night crowd, for the 'Transformation Scene: Burning GPO,' while the very amplifiers carrying Pearse's oration over the grave of Rossa were deafened in a mad roar of cheering that went on till the darkness came down and we had till the end of the next act to compose our features and look at our neighbours without embarrassment?

In my childhood I could remember the whole week a damn sight better than I can now, for I have learned enough arithmetic to know that I could not possibly have taken part in the Rising, which happened seven years before I was born.

When I was nine years old or so, I could have given you a complete account of what happened from Mount Street Bridge out to the Battle of Ashbourne, where I was giving Tom Ashe and Dick Mulcahy a hand. I could have told you how Seán Russell and I stopped them at Fairview, and could have given you a fuller description of Easter, 1916, than many an older man. You see, they were mostly confined to one garrison—I had fought at them all.

There was nothing remote about it. I grew up to be rather surprised by and condescending to any grown-up person who had not taken part in the Rising. I sorted out my uncles with garrisons: Uncle Michael, Uncle Peadar and my step-brother's father, Jack Furlong, were in Jacobs, with Paddy Manning, a native speaker from Kerry, and father-in-law of the writer Valentin Iremonger. Our breadman, who was called Georgie Manning, and no relation to Paddy. Our Uncle Joe was in the Post Office, and up in Nelson Street the whole family were feeding messengers and keeping a stopping place for despatch carriers, from my Aunt Maggie and my mother down to Lorcan and Rick Bourke, and Jimmy Kearney, who were expected to dodge round and in under the feet of enemy cordons as quick as schoolboy's impudence could carry them.

Jimmy Kearney is still in the communications business, but as a totally pacific telephone man below in Crown Alley.

I was in the Fianna with a boy from Mountjoy Street direction, who was called Finbar Howard, and his brother was killed in the Rising. I knew Pa Fox from Dunshaughlin, whose son was killed in it, and the Healys of Phibsboro Road, whose son, Seán, was the youngest Republican casualty, shot dead at the age of fifteen.

I had heard of Tom Clarke's gleeful remark, when the flag went down and they were marched to the Rotunda in defeat: 'God, it was great to see them run.' And I heard tell of how Charlie Goulding, an Old Invincible, pleaded with his sons, and their in-laws, the Costellos, to bring him to the Rising, though he died in his bed before the week was out. And wasn't the loveliest song of this day (or any other) Rising, 'The Tri-Coloured Ribbon,' written by my Uncle Peadar to my Aunt Eva?

They were all very busy getting everything right,
For the young and the old were both eager to fight,
Every man there, worked hard at his own barricade,
When the rifles rang out from the Dublin Brigade.

So they were, and on Tuesday morning Hanna Mortis was down at the GPO looking for her husband.

Stepping over a dead lancer or so, amidst the flame and shuddering of the blazing street, between shell-bursts, with machine guns tearing hell out of all round her, she shouts up at the shattered windows.

'Have yous got my Paddy in there?'

A horrified Volunteer shouts at her for God's sake to take herself out of that. A shell hits Laird's the chemist's, and when the smoke has cleared and the dust has settled he looks out again to see how many pieces Hanna is in.

She is still there, brushing the debris off herself, and shouts up,

'You needn't be so impiddent about it. I only wanted to know was he going to his work this morning.'

I'll sing you a song of a row in the town,
When the green flag went up, and John Bull's came down.
'Twas the neatest and sweetest thing ever you saw,
And they played the best game played in Erin go Bragh.

Our brave de Valera was down at Ringsend,
The honour of Ireland to hold and defend,
He had no veteran soldiers but Volunteers raw,
Playing sweet Mauser music for Erin go Bragh.

A great British Captain was raving that day,
Said he: 'Give me one hour and I'll blow them away.'
But a big Mauser bullet just stuck in his craw,
And he died from lead poisoning in Erin go Bragh.

Here's to Pearse and Connolly and Plunkett that died,
And Tom Clarke and MacDonagh, MacDermott, MacBride,
And here's to Seán Heuston, that gave one hurrah,
Then he faced the machine-guns for Erin go Bragh.

Here's a health to the men of the brave rank and file,
And the lion-hearted women of Erin's green isle,
Let true men salute them, with wonder and awe,
For they played the best game played in Erin go Bragh.

All glory to Dublin, 'tis hers the renown,
Through the long generations her fame will go down,
And children will tell how their forefathers saw
The red blaze of freedom in Erin go Bragh.

They played it all right, and some of them, like 'Mac Uí' Comerford, died above in the Union. Would it be too much to ask that those who survive are at least as well looked after as if they had fought for England?

Irish Press 11 April 1955

It's Torca Hill for beauty

One of my teachers was a young lady who was very refined.

This refined young lady teacher of mine came in one Monday morning and told us that she had spent the Sunday at Killiney.

'But,' said she, in tones of mournful refinement, 'it's ruined now with trippers. The place is full of them.'

Not knowing what she was talking about, but anxious to get in a bit of tee-hee before she'd ask me for an exercise that I hadn't done, I shot forward with fluent sleeveenery into the conversation.

'Ah, sure, teacher,' said I, 'isn't Dollymount the same, full of trippers. I was there yesterday with me da and me ma and Rory and Seán and Seamus and Brian and Dominic and Carmel in the pram, and it was rotten with trippers.'

'But Dollymount,' said my refined teacher, 'Dollymount is *for* trippers.'

I have never gone to Killiney since without thinking of her.

Sunday and Monday, I was out there. Looking out from the railway bridge at White Rock, along that curving beach and the wooded hills behind, it bears comparison with any part of the Côte d'Azur. Bernard Shaw said that the view from Torca Hill was so magnificent that no man that ever looked out on it was the same again. But the beach is not so good as at Portmarnock, or even at the strangely neglected seaside of Baldoyle.

Situated between Howth and Kilbarrack is the beach with the sea running up to the edge of the racecourse, and very convenient Billy Carroll and bookie says, for despairing fav. fanciers when the good thing drops dead a length from home.

Kilbarrack, my father always maintained, was the healthiest graveyard in the country, with the sea air. Last St Patrick's Day on the way to the races I looked out for the tri-colour that used to wave over the grave of Volunteer Dan Head killed at the Custom House. Never a funeral went out from the north side to Kilbarrack but the people would go over, after their own dead were buried, to gather round the flag and say a prayer for Dan Head. The ordinary people, without prompting from any organisation.

And before I go back the other side of the bay to Killiney, I may tell you that in Howth they have a paper of their own, in which is reported the wedding of a girl from the Hill. The affair was carried out with function and capernosity, by all accounts, but my colleague from the *Howth Review* is not going to accept anything on hearsay. He says:

'The honeymoon is being spent in Minorca. (Understood to be an island in the Mediterranean.)'

I hope it was there when the happy couple got to it.

Now, to get back to Killiney. At the top of the hill, in a park maintained by the ratepayers, there is a peculiar-looking relic of the days when an eccentric and charitable landlord could indulge his dull fancies cheaply, by getting the people to build follies and wonderful barns, and get a good name for himself as a philanthropist at the same time.

This object has a marble inscription at the top which says:

'LAST year being hard with the poor, the WALLS about these hills and the ETC erected by JOHN MAPAS, ESQ., June 1842.'

JOHN MAPAS and his ETC are bad enough, but could be left there as a curiosity and to remind the people of what our ancestors had to put up with; but another notice is a standing piece of impertinence on behalf of the late Herrenvolk. It says:

'Victoria Hill.

'Acquired by the Queen's Jubilee Association Dublin, the 21st June, 1887, the day appointed for the celebration of the reign of Queen Victoria, 30th June, by his Royal Highness Prince Albert Victor of Wales.'

Well, we may deplore JOHN MAPAS's taste in ETCs but at least the building of it might have saved some poor creature from the Famine. Queen Victoria's good deed for the day, during her most famous famine a few years later, was the presentation of five pounds to the Relief Fund. It was said she gave another five to The Dogs' Home, Battersea, the same day to prevent jealousy.

Irish Press 4 June 1955

Turnip boat

For some reason a friend of mine wanted to ship turnips from a Six Counties' port. He wanted to ship anything from a Six Counties' port because he wanted to sail into a British port with a British Customs manifest, or whatever Mac Lir would call it.

Our little ship was about the size of the Terenure bus. It was eighty-six tons in weight or capacity, gross or net. Again I leave it to the experts.

We sailed with a mixed crew. Some had been on a boat before, and more hadn't. I was betwixt and between. I did many's the trip on the *Larssen* and the *Royal Iris* as a bona-fide traveller, but had never actually rounded the Horn, or stifled me mainbrace or anything of that nature.

The real sailors were the Skipper, the mate, the fireman. The rest of the company were merchant adventurers along with the owner, and I was a merchant adventurer's labourer, so to speak.

The real sailors slept forrad, and we had accommodation aft, where, as Sammy Nixon said, villainy could be plotted in peace.

Sammy came aboard wearing rather tasty pin-striped kid gloves, and a Windsor knot of some dimensions. His hat he wore on the Kildare side, even in bed, for he had not a rib between him and heaven.

He had come straight from a pub in Belgravia, flown to Collinstown, and after a stop for refreshments in Grafton Street, or thereabouts, had come down by taxi to the North Wall where we had her tied up.

Sammy had never been on a boat of any description before, and till he had heard from Eddie, thought they'd been done away with, like the trams.

'Muscles' Morgan, his china, was due on a later plane, and what old Muscles would say when he saw this lot Sammy did not know.

Muscles when he arrived dressed in the same uniform as Sammy, all eight stone of him, said: 'Corsalawk, e'n it? Kookah er, Namber One, cock,' which he repeated many times during our subsequent voyages, and Eddie, Sammy, Muscles and I retired aft to drink rum, like sailors.

The sailors we left forrad, brewing their tea, darning their socks, winding the dockwatch and with infinite skill, putting little ships into bottles. There would be no shortage of bottles. Before we thought of calling the skipper we already had a couple of empties for the little ships to be put into them.

The Skipper fell to our level, through drinking, gambling and sniffing. Just common sniffing. I am not unacquainted with the national catarrh, but he was a most hangdog-looking man, with a sad puppy's face pleading for a friendship, or at least tolerance, and his shape and make was that of a Charles Atlas in reverse. And the whole world of ineffectual weakness was in that sniff.

Eddie picked him up in the West End, and brought him over with the boat.

He sniffed nervously to me that he had never been in Ireland before, though his family had a house in Mount Street, and if I possibly thought, if it would not, sniff, be too much, sniff, trouble could I, would I not, presuming on our short acquaintance, tell him how to get there? His father was born in it.

Better than that. I would bring him to it. And did, after a couple of stops at other points of interest on the way. And he cried and sniffed, and when I stood him with his back to Holles Street Hospital, he looked up along Fitzwilliam Square and Fitzwilliam Place, lit by the sun on the mountains behind the long range of golden Georgian brick, and wept again, and said there was not the like of it anywhere else.

So I got Eddie to call him down, and he sat in a corner and apologetically lowered an imperial pint of rum and hot orange. I think he took a subsidiary couple of rossiners to make up for the orange.

For if it's a thing I go in for in a human being it's weakness, I'm a divil for it. I thought of the Katherine Mansfield short story, where the 'Daughters of the Late Colonel' are afraid of the old chap, two days after his funeral, leaping out of the linen press on top of them, and one of them cries: 'Let's be weak, oh, please, let us be weak.'

He even sniffed an apology to Muscles and Sammy for their sea-sickness the first two days out, while they lay in their death agonies and shuddered from the cup of rum he would minister unto them.

He lowered it himself and weakly took himself up on deck to look for the Saltees. We had a reason for going to France, before the Six Counties manifest would be of use to us.

When we came back for our turnips, the final arrangements had to be made with what I will call the Turnip Board, and we marched up the main street of a northern port on Armistice Day.

Eddie went into a shop and came out with two big poppies. I shook my head.

'No bottle?' said I, in his native language.

'None of this old mallarkey,' said he, 'there's a reason why I must get a cargo of turnips off these geezers.'

'That's not what I mean. They won't fancy poppies.'

'This is "Northern Ireland", 'nt it? They're for the King and Queen and all that lark, 'nt they?'

'Not here. This is "Southern Northern Ireland".'

Eddie sighed. 'Only a nicker wasted,' and dropped his two ten-shilling poppies in the gutter. 'I get on. Mostly RCs here, eh?'

We met the chairman of the Turnip Board in an hotel and Eddie shook him by the hand.

'I think it's an 'orrible shame the way, the way these Protestants treat you 'ere, Mr MacConvery.'

Mr MacConvery's plum face turned blue, and his stomach went in and out at a hell of a lick.

'The cheek of you,' he croaked; 'my old friend,' he indicated a little man like an undertaker's clerk sitting nearby, 'Mr Macanaspie, re-spected member of the Presbyterian community, vice-chairman of the Turnip Board, we have it one year, they the next, chair and vice, turn an' turn about . . . I . . .'

His indignation collapsed for the want of breath, and I got a chance to explain that it was a joke, and it gave Eddie a chance to tell how he'd taken a prize in the Band of Hope himself.

And in the heel of the hunt we got the turnips and some months later, in the bar of the Latin Quarter, as us old seadogs hove to in there, Eddie remarked that Partition was strategically useful.

Irish Press 4 June 1955

The tinkers do not speak Irish

Round the corner, there, on the more literary page of this newspaper, it would be a reserved sin to pass any manner of a disrespectful remark about tinkers.

There's great tinker fanciers in them parts, as the poem says:
Alanna machree, now listen to me,
Me darlint go to res'
You're safe from harm, all snug and warm,
Wrapped up in your IRISH PRES'.

That's from the 'Tinker Ma to her Wee Warbler,' by Brian Mac Donogh Mac Sigger, translated by machinery from the original Irish of 'An Sleeveen Lobharach'.

No, if me life is to be taken and I'm to go in the midst of me sins for saying it. If I'm forever more to be denied the company of sonneteering civil servants, carolling customs men, brogueish brehons, I have to put all balladeering biromen right about this: *The Tinkers do not speak Irish.*

For the matter of that, it's little enough, any of them speak English.

'Tis many the good story you'll hear of them, mister honey, when the port is being passed around at dinner after the Petty Sessions, but though the company there, brilliant and gay, may have the lives and souls of the Munster Circuit on it, they will hardly have the principal qualification for knowing the tinkers or anyone else. They haven't lived with them.

I have. In a house twenty-five or thirty years ago, when the MacGowans came up for the Tailteann Games.

They couldn't pitch a wagon nearer Croke Park than thirteen, Russell Street, which was my granny's house, and was situated on the site of the present Rowan's Seed Factory, with the DWD at the rear and Mountjoy Brewery on our right flank, as you look down from the North Circular Road.

My grandfather was a moderate man, who believed in having a pint and a half one, every ten minutes, but not making a beast of yourself, and worked hard as a painting contractor, and had Number Thirteen well kept up, with a shut hall door, grocers' porters calling with the messages, shout down the area and do not beat the knocker off, a beautiful double breasted hatstand in the hall, which was also adorned with a reproduction of Turner's famous picture of a naval engagement being fought in a hayfield . . . at least I thought it was hay, though an eminent English art cricketer has since told me it's the Atlantic ocean . . . faced by a picture of Smith, the Brides in the Bath murderer, whose likeness taken from the *News of the World*, had been framed and hung by my grand aunt Maggie Jack, under the mistaken impression that it was a picture of a Fenian.

My grandfather was down the country painting a cathedral in county Wexford, leaving his own beautiful two pair apartment vacant.

My grandmother looked out sadly at the milling crowds of people all round Croker and they willing to pay anything to be near the Games. Sadly she turned them away from her door, when Mrs MacGowan a Queen Tinker came up and tempted her with a free fortune telling in which she was to marry for the third time, a paisley shawl and five pounds for accommodation for all hands, jennets and Christians.

That passed off very civil, though it was a bit disturbing when they got the jennet up to bed. He slept, under it, and though he didn't make any more noise in his sleep than my granny, once he got there, it was the rooly-booly getting him there that was a bit noisy.

'Get up there, can't you, come on, now you cross-born,' this that and the other, and whack! he'd get a belt where it wouldn't blind him, till at last he was settled down and we could rest in peace.

Till my grandfather came home all of a sudden. He said he couldn't miss the rodeo, if you please. The rest of the Tailteann Games he didn't mind, nor he wasn't over-partial to seeing John Devoy, the Lord have Mercy on them all, but the rodeo he would not miss.

Luckily, he was late coming in, and not noticing much of what was going on, having spent a deal of time nourishing himself, eating and drinking in Lacey's of Gorey, and points north, but in the morning he woke up, and went out on the landing.

The jennet was standing the length of the stairs, with his forepaws stretched in front of him, looking up at Angelica Kauffman's ceiling. Then he lowered his eyes and looked into my grandfather's, and my grandfather looked into his, like Garbo looking into Robert Taylor's.

'May God protect us,' said my grandfather, in terror, not unmixed with amazement, but mixed with it. 'Stephen Francis,' he pleaded.

My own father came out and asked my grandfather what was up.

'I don't know,' said my grandfather, 'what is it, you?'

'A jennet,' says my father.

'That He may be praised—now and forever more,' says my grandfather. 'I thought I was in the rats.'

'In the jennets,' laughed my father, with loveable repartee.

Later on, I heard my grandfather and the MacGowans speaking together and it wasn't Irish, they were speaking, nor English.

Irish Press 27 August 1955

Nuts from the Crimean War

Round our way there were many candidates for the brain garage. They were victims of the Great War, as it used to be called; the Black and Tan War, the Civil War, and the Economic War, when we were all a bit hatcha from eating free beef.

Mrs Leadbeater could have been nuts from the Crimean War—she was old enough—but like many another she was mad in her own right.

Her sister, Mrs Moneypenny, never recovered from a trip she'd made to Howth in the late summer of 1912, when she came back believing she had been turned into a lobster, and was ever after apprehensive of the death she would suffer if the people decided to eat her.

The sight of a pot of water, hot or cold, was enough to send her screeching from the kitchen. When she was finally brought back she would appeal to all and sundry not to put her in the pot.

Her first appeals were on the grounds of compassion, but she varied it by pointing out to the people that they wouldn't get much off her, anyway.

In Summerhill there was a German fishmonger called Frankenstein for short, and he used to run in the back of the shop when he saw her coming and leave the messenger boy to face her.

Sorrowfully she'd look down at the bright red bodies and claws on the slab, getting her emotions under control to give her screech in at the fugitive fishmonger: 'Murderer! Torturer! Who murdered my poor brothers and sisters!' And with a look in the direction of the dressed crab, 'and cousins!'

Then there was a Mr Aloysius Giltrap, who used to clap in the chapel and provoked Sergeant Cloonoe, who used to get his wife out on the floor at half-two in the morning doing foot-drill and bayonet practice with the sweeping-brush. But personally, I always thought that the Corcorans of the back kitchen, Number Ten, beat them all over the distance.

Mrs Corcoran was an old lady of some seventy summers, which, counting the winters, would leave her at the time of which I speak about a hundred and forty, which is what she looked and not a day more.

Her son Paddins was a sort of Neo-Old IRA man and dressed for the part. He wore a cap, a sports coat with leather buttons and split up the middle and knee breeches. He resembled very much a picture of a fearsome character depicted on the Cumann na nGaedheal election posters of the time, which read: 'Vote for Us and Keep the shadow of the Gunman from your Home.'

Very little chisellers like myself thought it was Paddins Corcoran on the poster and gave him great respect, but the big fellows used to greet him on the corner with salutes and standing to attention, and making him reports from the First Brigade, the Second Brigade, the Boys' Brigade and the Fire Brigade.

Poor Paddins would take it all for in the real, whereas it was only in the cod, and on Bodenstown Sunday he was a sight to free Ireland. With only a look at him, the British would have given back the Six Counties and thrown the Isle of Man in for good measure.

He wore his cap, but turned back to the front with the peak down the back of his neck to show that he was ready for active service, and a pair of leggings he'd borrowed off L. S. D. Regan, the dairyman from Santry, also known on a less national scale as Long Skinny Dominic, whence the initials.

He also had a bandolier, grimly bulging with rolled pieces of paper and a water-bottle, over the sports coat.

At one of the street battles in Cathal Brugha Street that helped to pass the depression for the people, Paddins shouted up to a well-known public figure who was trying to address a meeting, 'You have the best of men in your jails, and I dare you to take me now.'

I may not, nor no one belonging to me, have agreed with his opinions, but the aforesaid figure was a Dubliner and seldom short of an answer. He leaned down from the platform to answer Paddins. 'I am not,' he said, 'a collector of curios.'

But with a fine disregard for the late Civil War, the chaps on the corner didn't mind getting it up for Joshua Carroll, who was a part-time soldier in the Government Army.

Joshua was called up for training a number of times a year and had to go away to a camp. During the winter he stood in the evening-time on the corner dressed in his green uniform, which for some reason had blue epaulettes. The big fellows had us chisellers trained to sing at him:

'If you're fed up with life,
And you don't want a wife,
Do what Joshua did,
Join the Militia . . .'

Myself and my brothers joined in this, with function and capernosity, as true little Republicans, apart from the excitement of annoying someone that was doing us no particular harm—an occupation indulged in, with less excuse, by many of us in later life—and were somewhat taken aback when Paddins Corcoran chased us and went to give our Rory a clout.

We expressed our indignation at such treachery, but Paddins said, 'I respect Joshua, as one soldier to another,' returned to the corner and saluted Joshua, who returned the salute, when both forces 'reconoythered' the position to see if they could make up between them the price of two pints.

Irish Press 3 September 1955

I'm a British object, said the Belfast-man

'I'm a British object,' said this elderly Belfast-man to me, one Twelfth of July, a long time ago. We were in the little village of Millisle, near Donaghadee in the County Down. We had gone out there to pass the beautiful day of high summer like true Irishmen, locked in the dark snug of a public house.

The Belfast-man was an inebriate of some standing, whose politics were purely alcoholic. He was what they call in the North-East a wine victim, and carried his affection for things British to drinking port from the vineyards of Hoxton, and sherry from Tooting Bec, at five shillings the ten-glass bottle. He had come down for the day from the city and scandalized the assembled Orangemen by his reluctance to drink porter.

That lovely summer's day I'll remember too for the singing of an old man from Millisle. 'The Bright Silvery Light of the Moon' and the 'Yellow Rose of Texas' he sang, and disappointed me because he

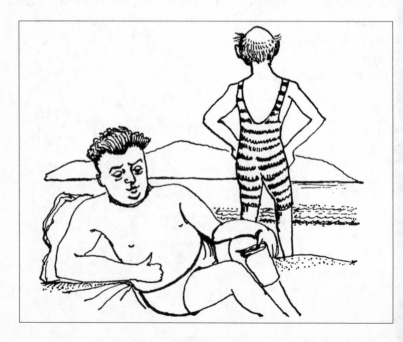

didn't sing something more Orange. The nearest he got to 'party politics' was a song about the Crimean War that went to the air of 'The
Rakes of Mallow':

All drawn up, Britannia's sons
Faced the Russian tyrant's guns,
And bravely dared his shells and bombs,
On the Bonny Heights of Alma.

We had a great day of singing and drinking and eating, and though
I did feel a bit shamed by the bright sunshine when we came out
blinking into it at closing-time, it wasn't long before we got indoors
again.

Next morning I didn't feel so good, but in the summer-time nothing lasts long, and I was swimming around the harbour like a two-
year-old and was shortly joined by a young man from the Shankill,
who confided in me that he could always 'tell a Fenian'.

'And how,' said I, lying on the sea, *bolg in airde*, and looking up at
the sun, 'do you manage that?'

'Ah know them be their wee button noses.'

I felt my own snitcher, and reflected that it would make a peculiar
surrealistic sort of wee button.

The British Object was not so politically unaware as I'd thought.
He too appeared, ready for the waves, dressed in a high-necked black
costume that bore some resemblance to a habit, and emblazoned with
an enormous orange crest with the inscription 'True to You', and sur-
mounted not as you might expect by a ten-glass bottle of Liverpool
champagne, but by a head of the late King Edward the Seventh.

He dived in and thrashed about like a man in the jigs, and I confi-
dently expected the sea to become wine-coloured after him, like 'the
wine-coloured ocean' of Homer.

I'd not have believed a person if they'd told me that summer would
ever end, or I'd have believed them as one believes a mathematical
proposition, from the mind out only.

It seems years ago since the summer when we were crowded jam-
tight from Merrion to Seapoint, and half doped from the sun when
the pavements of Grafton Street were like the top of an oven, and you

had to dodge into Mac's and get yourself on the high stool for the safety of the soles of your feet.

Is it only a short time ago that I stood at ten o'clock of an evening in the little town of Callan, and went over to read the inscription over the house of Humphrey O'Sullivan, the Gaelic diarist and poet, now most appropriately a fish-and-chip shop?

Poets are great one-and-one men. I don't know about diarists.

I'd sample the chips another time, with a bit of ray, but that evening I had eaten at Mrs Coady's, and after her huge rounds of prime beef and fresh vegetables you wouldn't be in humour of anything for a good while.

I'd come out from her place trying to remember the name and getting mixed up, muttering in a daze of good living, like an incantation, charm or spell, the words 'Mrs Callan of Coady', I mean 'Mrs Coady of Callan'.

And the Guard I met, that told me of raiding a pub after hours and finding three men in it. And the publican starts 'ah-sure-ing' him that they're only friends that he wants to give a farewell drink to, because they're off to Lourdes the following day.

The Guard says all right, and not be too long and, going out, meets three others on their way to the hall door.

Regretting his previous mildness, he enquires sarcastically:

'And I suppose you three are going to Lourdes, too?'

'Musha no, sergeant, *a mhic*, we're going to Knock.'

Irish Press 8 October 1955

Our budding genius here

'I'm suspended that much, I don't know whether I'm coming or going,' said Mrs Brennan. 'If only we knew what she was going to do, one way or another, but she'll have to make up her mind about him. I can't stand being suspended any more; can you, Mr Cripping, sir?'

'If we only knew,
What she was going to do,
Did she but reach a decision
And end our surmission,'

quoted Crippen, adding: 'Them lines is be Yeets.' He turned to me. 'I suppose our budding genius here—'

'That's what he is, Mr Cripping. A pudding cheenis. I knew his poor granny, God be good to her, and she was another, and never used any but white snuff, so she didn't, isn't that right, Maria Concepta?'

'Trew, trew, trew, Mrs Brenning, ma'am,' croaked Maria Concepta,

'but go on, Mr Cripping, sir, with the poetery. Carry on with the coffing, the corpse will walk.'

'I was going to ask Behing here, this honorary journalist, whether he was familiar with that poem be Yeets that begins "O, to have a little house".'

'The Scotch House,' muttered Maria Concepta. 'He has you there. Behing here, onrey churnalist, and pudding cheenyuss, you've the shape of wan, anyway, what matter.'

'Maria Concepta, you're rambling that far, you'll be bona fide in a minute,' said Mrs Brennan. 'Get a grip of yourself be the two hands and pull yourself together.'

'I can't help it, Mrs Brenning, ma'am. I'm in suspenders over this other one. Will she or won't she?'

'We're all the one way,' said Mrs Brennan. '"I ahpreeshy ate your pree dick ah ment," as the gentleming said and him trying to get the hot sassidge outa the coddle, but that's not to say, be the same toking of regard, that we're all to drop down dead of the drewth while she makes up her mind. This is the hour of decishing—'

'Brought to yous each evening be the—'

'Maria Concepta, you're wandering again, what are you having?—that'll bring her to.'

'I'll have a drain of the other, Mrs Brenning ma'am. Me nerves is gone from the straying.'

'It's a straying on all of us. Michael, will you have the deezensy to stop picking your nose there and do what you're supposed to do be the powers of your special exempting—to wit, supply persons lawfully attending said fair and market with a gargle?'

'All right, all right,' said Michael, 'and no word about him and her yet?'

'Not a word,' said Crippen. 'She's gone away to the country for a few days, I heard.'

'Ah, now, when all is said and done—a little sup of peppermint in that, Michael, eef you pleeze—it's hard on her. I feel it as if it was me daughter,' said Mrs Brennan. 'Wimming feels for wimming, isn't that right, Maria Concepta?'

'You could sing it, Mrs Brenning, and play it on a mellow-jing if you had an air to it. Wimming feels for wimming—and, of course, when all is said and done, it's for love. I remember my poor fellow, I often told yous, Cripping and Behing, no need to tell Mrs Brenning there, she knew him well—'

'Is it poor Gobbles, Maria Concepta? Didn't I separate him and me own poor dear deeparted, the night they came out of the hot meat shop in Thomas Court Bawn and went to fight a jewel with a backbone each?'

'I met him, the Lord have mercy on him, and he coming out of the Somali village, the year of the exhibishing. I sees this pig me, as black as your boot, and pouring sweat, though it wasn't for all he was wearing, after doing the war dance of the Mosambongas, and he runs after me with the spear. I screeched mela murders and ran like the hammers of hell, with him after me till he got me in a corner, and I near went in a weakness. I thought of offering him me glass beads from off me neck, but they were a pair I borrowed off me sister, Teasy, and I was more afraid of her; but I looked into his black face, and his eyes rolling in his head, and I moaned and said, "You Zulu," and I was going to say, "Me too," God forgive me, when he caught me pashing at lee to his heaving boozem, and whispered, "Would you ever go down as far as Searson's for three glasses of porter in a jug?"'

'Ah, yes, the course of trew love is ever up a hill,' sighed Mrs Brennan. 'Mr Cripping, sir, you have sorceresses of informayshing; do you think she will or she willn't?'

'I don't know,' said Crippen. 'I heard the clergy say she shouldn't, and some of the people says she should, and I don't like this going off to the country for a few days—'

But there was a commotion in the street outside and Mrs Brennan dashed out in the middle of his sentence, close followed by Maria Concepta. Crippen and I were making hurried efforts to finish our pints when they burst back in the door, just as quick.

'It's all over,' said Mrs Brennan, 'she's not going to do it. I'm nearly weak, so I am.'

'So am I,' muttered Maria Concepta, reaching her hand out on the counter for a tumbler to grip.

'I'll stand,' said Michael. 'What are yous for?'

Maria Concepta struggled to the door again. 'They're coming down here—her and him linking her. Here they are.' In great excitement she held open the door, and in came a woman with a black eye, followed by a man.

'I couldn't do it in the finish,' said the black-eyed lady. 'Not when I saw that ould Bridewell. I couldn't charge him; not if he gave me a black eye in every part of me body—and out in the country, in the sister's place in East Finglas, I missed him.'

'And I missed her,' muttered your man.

'Maybe she won't miss you the next time with a pot,' said Mrs Brennan severely.

'I suppose,' said Crippen, 'it's better to be fighting than to be lonely.'

Irish Press 5 November 1955

The fun of the panto

'Fun with vulgarity' was the motto of our pantomime. It opened on St Stephen's Night, feast of St Stephen, and I never heard it called Boxing Day.

For long weeks before, the whole of the North Circular, from one side to the other, was a seething mass of intrigue and allying and counter-allying, crossing and double-crossing, that would have done credit to the United Nations, if such a thing had been going at the time.

At first it was the City side against the Croke Park side. Not all of these people knew one another, and indeed there were sore hearts in one street, which was highly respectable and in flats rather than rooms, at the thoughts of having to get up on the same stage as people from our street, but we had the good singers, and also, if we were not adequately represented we would not come, except to make trouble, and whatever our shortcomings in the matter of shut hall doors or prams and bikes in the hall, it was generally recognised that we were good at making trouble.

But by the time the rehearsals had started the quarrels and jealousies had reached an intensity that had ceased to regard any considerations of class or social position.

Many a life-long enmity was firmly founded on the question of whose little girl was to play a babe in the wood or whose big girl was to be a principal boy.

By the time the curtain was ready to go up, the hall was grimly seething in a mood far too serious for anything so frivolous as fun, leave alone vulgarity.

The stewards were the subject of intense, whispered discussion, frequently libellous.

'Did you see who they had taking in the money in the one-and-sixpennies?—old Baldy Conscience.'

'That's right. The same fellow used to go be the name of Sawdust Pocket when he was on the chapel door.'

'And sure if he's bad, the fellow who's with him is worse. They put the Boy Scouts on the door of the chapel while they were on holidays, and they got that much extra they never let them pair back.'

'It's up there on the stage they ought to be, giving a conjuring turn, now you see it, now you don't.'

'Sh-sh, the curtain's going up.'

The band played its opening bars and the girls went into their line number, singing one of many songs, all of which went like this:

'Oh, happy, happy, day and we hope you may
Enjoy our little show tonight,
That it may your heart delight, and make you merry and
bright too-o-o-o-ni—ght.'

There was applause then from such of the audience as were personal supporters of members of the chorus. The rest waited for their own nominations to come out and contented themselves with a thin bringing together of the palms of the hands, but discreetly so as not to make noise. There was usually comment on the chorus ladies.

'I see that one of the Hegartys is out again. That blondy one there.'

The speaker's eldest daughter had been kept out of the chorus and a scalded heart will say many's the thing. 'I'd be long sorry to see any girl of mine got up in that get-up.'

'All the same, it's wonderful how she's able to get round the stage for a woman of her years. She's deserving of a diamond jubilee presentation, I don't care what anyone says—forty years she's getting up on them boards. Oh, yous can laugh and sneer, jibe and jeer, but which of us would be that active at her age?'

Later in the show the court scene was in full swing.

Judge: 'How would you like your poor mother to be here and see you in the dock?'

Prisoner: 'Ah sure the bit of an outin' of the Joy would do her good.'

In the audience, herself is putting himself through it for laughing, in burning, vitriolic whispers, till he squirms in the seat.

'You cur to go laughing at the red-nosed ruffian and his low jokes about the Joy. Of course, you and him could shake hands on knowing more about that place than most people—and you hadn't as much as a grin on you when your daughter, our own child, was up there singing "I wish I had a little cat". But wait.'

'Miss Eyelash Nick Gabbin—Nick I mean—she's a pain—'

A fierce jab of a programme in the ear attracts the attention of the speaker.

'Who are you to call my daughter, *Éilis Nic Gabhann*, a pain?'

'I was only saying she was a pianist. That's what they have her down here as. And I was only saying "Nick" is a funny name for a girl.'

'You're only showing your ignorance of your own language—that's her name in Irish, *gan teanga, gan tír*, you perisher.'

A few nights later we'd be all out to get the paper and read about it.

'. . . To introduce the various items there was the popular Dublin master of ceremonies, Paddy (Whacker) Whelan. The accompanists were Johnny Nola (piano) and Bill Gannon (drums).

'The popular song 'I like bananas, because they have no bones' was a big hit, as was the song-scene with the sunflowers.'

Irish Press 17 December 1955

Overheard in a bookshop

'Could I have a Dinneen?' asked this respectable-looking party in the bookshop.

'No, sir, we wouldn't have such a thing,' answered the lady assistant. 'I don't know would you get one in Dublin at all. Ectu-ahly,' she finished, 'it's a kind of Cork hoarze doovray, isn't it?'

Your man went off in some puzzlement, and the lady assistant remarked to her young man, elegantly: 'Coming up here and the mark of the stir-about spoon still in their mouth, and looking for them things in a bookshop. You could easy see it was not a pork butcher's. But maybe he thinks it's like the shops back home in the bog where they sell you *Old Moore's Almanac* and a pound of black and white pudding off the one counter.'

Her young man murmured something appropriate, and continued to gaze into her eyes, long and pleadingly. She returned to their own conversation and shook her head for the fourth or fifth time.

'Ignayzeous, I'm really very, very sorry, but I deffiny could not make it. Genuine, I couldn't,' she sighed, 'not but what I'd a loved to.'

An old gentleman came up to ask for a New Testament.

'Desperate sorry, I am, sir,' said Ida Lufftoo, 'but I am afraid it's not out yet. We have the old one, of course, but I suppose you've read that.'

The old gent looked at her in some dismay and retreated towards the door.

'Cheek and imperance of them old fellows when you go to give them a peas of information. Another fellow comes to me yesterday, a Northern by the sound of him, and he asks for a book about gorilla dazes in Ireland. I told him I'd never seen gorillas dazed, or any other way, in Ireland. Maybe they have them in Ulster, but if so, I said, that was the place to keep them. Then another pair comes in, Yanks they were be the sound of them, and ask me did I know Joyce is useless. I told them I didn't care whether he was or not, not knowing the man, T.G. One fellow has the common gall to laugh up into my face and tell me that was the sharpest crack he'd heard from a European.

'"Go 'way, you dirty low cur," said I, "to insult a lady. I'm no European, but an Irish girl, bred, born and reared in Donnelly's Orchard."'

Her young man muttered something fierce, but she waved her hand deprecatingly.

'That's all right, Ignayzeous, what you'd a done if you'd a been here, but you're like the *Garda Seo Caughyeh*, never where you're wanted. Then another fellow comes in and asks me for the new Greene, and I directed him to the top of Grafton Street and said he might do the best he could with the old one, because it was the only one I'd heard of in these parts, unless they'd have a new green in Ballyfermot or Donnycarney, out at the new houses, but I'd not know much about them places—ours is a purchase house, fifty pound down and you own it in 2006, if God spares us.

'Then there was an old chap in a Teddy Boy suit, velvet collar and all, drainpipes, and I don't know who he thought he was fooling. Going round in that get-up like a fellow of eighteen and I declare he was seventy if he was an hour, and he tries to get off his mark, if you please, asking me if I liked Kipling.

"'How could I know?" I asks, "when I never kippilled, and if I did it would be someone more me equals than you."

'And that put him in his place, I can tell you. He wasn't long clearing off. And all these dead-and-alive old books, you'd be lost for bit of a read only I do bring me *True Romances* with me. I'll be out of this place after the Christmas rush, anyway. I went back to the fellow in the Labour and he says to me: "I thought you *liked* working in a bookshop? You said you worked in one for three years."

"'A bookshop?" says I. "I told you I worked in the cook shop, in the biscuit factory, where they fill cakes and biscuits with jam and suchlike when they come out of the bakehouse."

"'Oh, is that so?" says he. "My mistake; well, keep your mouth shut till the first week in January and let on you can read and write."

"'You're desperate funny, you are," says I. "You're that sharp you'll cut yourself. I can read as good as you," and I read him a real high-class bit out of a book I borrowed here—the real classical, it is, all knowledge, and I read him a bit that stuck him to the ground.

"'Ah, my precious little girl, for God's sake cast occasionally a word or look of encouragement from your velvety lips or saddened eyes! Don't, my treasured hope, don't allow the slightest frown ever formed by the merest movement of Nature to dwell on your sinless brow, else I die. Yes, by Venus; ere I'd yield to have you torn from my arms of lifelong companionship, I'd resign my rights of existence to a region of undying flame.'"

She put down her book, and smiled gently at Ignayzeous's praises.

A tall lady of foreign, almost diplomatic appearance approached, and with an apologetic smile asked Ida if the Everyman edition of *Anna Karenina* was in stock.

Ida smiled back, interrogatively. 'Urm? Annakarra urm?'

'Tolstoy's *Anna Karenina*,' said the lady.

Ida nodded mysteriously and smiled her inscrutable smile. '*An bhfuil cead agam dul amach?*' she asked.

The lady looked at her and at Ignayzeous, and said, 'Quite—er—thank you.'

Ida's gaze followed her up the shop. 'It doesn't do to let yourself down before these foreigners. When they speak to me in their language I believe in answering them in mine.'

Then her eye took me in. 'Just a minute, Ignayzeous.' To me: 'Did you want to buy something?'

'Well, I was just having a look around,' said I. 'I was just—'

She gently but firmly removed the volume from my lifeless fingers and smiled but shook her head. 'Sorry, but no free reads.'

I nodded desperately and turned in the direction of the door, her voice trailing after me.

'I may be only here for a week, Ignayzeous, but I don't want the shop robbed *barefaced!*

Irish Press 7 October 1956

The hot malt man and the bores

'"Wipe your bayonet, Kinsella, you killed enough."'

'Go on,' says I.

'That's genuine,' said Kinsella, 'that's what Lord Roberts says to me in Blamevontame in 'nought one. I knew him before, of course, from the time we were in Egg Wiped. "Shifty Cush" says Bobs, when he seen me on parade, "is that you, Kinsella?" "It is," says I, coming smartly to attention. "Who were you expecting?"

'"You've killed enough of bores," says Bobs.'

There was a sharp-featured gentleman sitting beside us having a drop of malt, hot. A great odour of cloves and old Irish rose from him as he turned round. He glared at Kinsella in a nationalistic fashion. 'That did you great credit, I'm sure. The bores never done this little country any harm for you to be killing them. Are you an Irishman?'

'I am,' says Kinsella. 'Are you a bore?'

'*Ná bac leis* whether I am or not,' says Hot Malt. 'The bores was

always good friends of this little country, and I don't see what call you had to go killing them.'

The Bottle of Stout man glanced nervously up from his bus guide and spoke querulously at us. 'Sure what's the good of arguing over that now? Wouldn't they all be dead of old age be this time, anyway?'

'I don't see why they should be,' said Hot Malt. 'This mercenary foe of theirs is alive yet.'

'Look at here,' says Kinsella. 'I'm no Mendecency foe of anyone. Maybe you know more about the Mendecency Institution than anyone else in this lounging bar.'

The Bottle of Stout man glanced again at his bus guide and called the assistant. 'How much is your clock fast?'

'The usual ten minutes, Mister O'.'

'I see, I see; bring us another bottle.' Then he fell to anxious calculations. 'It'd leave the Park gate at eight-forty and to the Pillar at eight-forty-eight, say, and . . .' He glanced round again and we saw the front of a bus come past the window. The Bottle of Stout man fell to the floor like a trained guerilla fighter and cowered below the level of the window.

The bus drew alongside the stop outside the pub and its top floor was on a dead level with the lounge in which we sat. The narrowness of the street made ourselves and the passengers intimate spectators of each other.

Only one of them took advantage of the proximity thus afforded: a hatched-faced oul' strap who swept the features of each of us with a searing sharpness and then, not altogether satisfied with what she'd seen, nodded grimly and almost threateningly as the bus bore her off.

'Eh,' says Kinsella, 'that was a dangerous-looking oul' one that looked in at us off the bus—the one with the face of a DMP man.'

The Bottle of Stout man rose to his feet, and after a look out the window, turned to Kinsella, who nodded and said, 'You didn't miss much there, she's a right hatchet, whoever she is.'

'Excuse yourself,' said the Bottle of Stout man, 'she is my wife, and I'll thank you to keep a civil tongue in your head.' He spoke round at the company. 'You can't expect a man to put up with remarks like that about the woman he loves.'

Heads were nodded approvingly, and Kinsella was in some confusion.

'How was I to know she was your wife? And how did you know yourself it was her I was talking about? You were sitting on the floor and didn't see her.'

'I recognised her from your description,' said the Bottle of Stout man, with the quiet dignity of a trained mind.

An elderly lady in the corner shook her head and murmured enigmatically into her port: 'As the ole opera says, "What the eye doesn't see the heart won't grieve for." I love you because you love her. Love's young dream, as I always said about my poor spowce: "Better the divil you know than the one you don't."'

'But anyway,' says Kinsella, resuming his conversation with me, 'the first man I sees at zero hour one-two—this was in the next war—was Jowls Loughrey, of the Dirty Shirts.

'"Halt," says he, "who goes there?"

'"It's me, Jowls," says I. "Whacker Kinsella from Messer Street—down beside the hospital."

'"Don't be so familiar with your 'Jowls'," says Jowls. "How do I know you're not German?"

'"I can't speak a word of German," says I. "I'm from Messer Street."

'"That doesn't prove anything," says Jowls, "I'm from Francis Street and I can't speak a word of French—howsomeever I'll take your word for it. The attack is off. We can't go over the top kicking the football in front of us tonight."

'"Why not?" says I. "The men in my spittoon was looking forward to the bit of exercise."

'"They're after losing the ball," says Jowls.'

Just at that moment the Bottle of Stout man, after a hurried look at his bus guide and at the clock, fell to the ground, swift as before.

'Like one of them syrup-pots,' said Kinsella admiringly.

But was not swift enough.

The lady shouted in from the top of the bus.

'I saw you,' she screeched, 'dodging down there, hiding on the floor. Making a jeer of your poor wife with your drunken bowseys of companions.' We all visibly blenched and cowered down, not on the floor altogether with the Bottle of Stout man, but with our faces not far off it. 'I know yous, you low lot. Tell him to get up off the floor now the bus is moving.'

It moved and we rose again.

'Don't mind me asking you,' asked the Hot Malt of the Bottle of Stout man. 'Why is it you don't go in another pub where she can't see you?'

The Bottle of Stout man sighed. 'You must forgive a sentimental old fool.'

'Certainly, certainly so,' muttered Kinsella, 'as an old soldier, I concur.'

The Bottle of Stout man wiped his eyes. 'This is how we met. She looked in at me off the top of a tram. I'll never forget it.'

Said the Hot Malt, 'Neither will we.'

Irish Press 14 January 1956

My great red racing bike

This wintery weather reminds me of Dún Laoghaire.

Not, I hasten to add, that there's anything more wintery about the Dún than any place else this time of the year. The sea may lash up and over the East Pier, but then with my own two eyes I've seen the blue-clad Corporation employees of a famous Riviera town collecting newly fallen snow and throwing it into the Mediterranean. And a tourist nearly going in after it for trying to take a snapshot.

But when I was a young house-painting fellow of eight stone or so, and that's not today nor yesterday, taking one thing with another, weight for age, I was the possessor of a red racing bicycle called, if I remember rightly, a Phoenix, and inherited by me from my brother. His house-painting activity had taken him by train and car round the province of Connacht, from Boyle Cathedral to the Irish College in Tourmakeady, County Mayo.

He fell a total of more than a hundred feet in those two places, so his perambulations had something of the quality of a circus tour.

Of the bicycle I was very proud and a very skilful cyclist in traffic. I could get from the city to Dun Laoghaire while you'd be saying Lennox Robinson.

So when my employer wanted some stuff to be brought out to a job in the Borough, I took the tram fare but used the bicycle to get out there.

Which is how I came to have a shilling on a Tuesday. It was the month of January and fairly cold in the morning but nothing exceptional about it, when I was starting off, but going through Ballsbridge it began spitting snow-water, and by the time I was at Blackrock the real genuine undiluted stuff was coming down in soft flakes, mild and gentle like a talk about Partition on the Third Programme. And by the time I got into Dún Laoghaire I was pushing through a blizzard.

The door of the house we were doing up was opened for me by an elderly painter, who was doing the job on his own. He was a native of the Channel Islands and went by the name of Janey.

I am not inventing this name. Poor Janey is no longer at this end of the plank, but I often wondered afterwards who did invent it. Maybe it was a corruption of his name in French.

'Come in, come in, young man, you are welcome,' said Janey. 'It's cold, isn't it?'

I shook myself like a whippet and admitted that it sure was, that you could play a melodeon to that.

'You 'ave terrible journey out to thees place,' said Janey. He always kept up a sort of a French fur-trapper's accent. The boss said that the old ones in the good-class trade liked it. I shook myself and nodded. 'You poor peeg,' said Janey.

Then after a minute or two he asked me, 'W'y you no come out in the . . . er . . . what you call tram-care?'

I told him I did not come out in the what-you-call-tram-care because I had a bike and wanted the shilling for myself. He nodded vigorously at this.

After we had a drop of tea and a bit of bread and brawn, Janey said it was no good my going back to the shop in that class of weather. I could get into stripping a room.

I went up to one of the upper rooms with stockbrush and scraper and set to work, but first I had to take up some linoleum.

This was a hazardous business for me. I never could resist reading old newspapers, and for me to raise a piece of old linoleum was like opening the door of a library.

I promised myself that I would only read a little bit, that I would just glance at the papers before I threw them into the snow outside, but when I raised the linoleum and saw the headline: 'Viceroy's visit to Grangegorman. Vicereine waves green linen handkerchief, scenes of mad enthusiasm,' I was lost and read it inch by inch, through the serial, 'Pretty Kitty'.

For new readers:

Lord Maulverer has fallen in love with pretty Kitty Hackett, daughter of Honest Tom Hackett, a country butcher. She helps her father in the slaughter-house and one day she is busily gutting when an anxious moo is heard. . .

Till at last Janey came into the room and caught me there. The old English drop-pattern paper unscarred by hand of mine as I bent over the morning paper for Tuesday, 12th June 1901.

'So,' he moaned in his saddest Quebec accent. 'You 'ave down nowthing, no?'

'No,' said I, shamefaced.

'So,' said Janey. 'You are 'ere 'alf-day and you 'ave down nowthing. You come 'ere at 'alf-nine. That is right. On bicycle.' At this point his face increased. 'You 'ave mawnay?'

'That's right,' says I, 'I've a shilling.'

It seems Janey could do with the loan of a shilling; no sooner said than done. He went down the stairs with my shilling and I went back on my floor to my papers.

But I misjudged him, even though it was a deal from my point of view.

At half past two he came back and gave me five shillings. He was all smiles, but said, 'Now we do some graft; yes, no?' I agreed yes, no, it wouldn't kill us once in a way.

When we quit that night Janey told me he'd backed Pappegeno II, which won at a hundred-to-six—in a blizzard.

'In the boogies I did it. They 'ave boogies 'ere too,' said Janey. 'Jus' like 'ome in Daublin.'

Irish Press 21 January 1956

Dialogue on literature and the hack

A voice (hoarse, relentless): 'Where were you in 'sixteen?'

'I wasn't born till 'twenty-three.'

A.V.: 'Excuses . . . always excuses.'

('You borrowed that from *Living with Lynch*.' 'I stole it, sir. An artist never borrows.')

A mirthless laugh rang through the snug at the far end of the shop. A shudder ran through me, and I ventured to the side door to have a look in the mirror, and a better view of the source of that awful sound (the mirthless laugh, I mean).

I knew the voice only too well, and the face and all.

It was the face of the Rasher Cambel, the Dolphin's Barn genius.

'Well,' he looked round at me, 'hack.'

'I was a hack,' says I, 'before you came up.'

I gazed down at my vis-à-vis, as the man said; he could not deny it. (At fifty, George Moore learned the comfort of semi-colons; us National schoolboys picks it up a bit earlier).

'My friend, Ma Loney, ah dear heavens,' says the Rasher, in the one breath and looking very hard at the two fellows out of the Artists' Fellowship; these were two youths out of the Corporation, and looked hard at me when he said these words, 'was a liar.'

'Shut up your big mouth now,' says Mister Moo, as he is called for short. 'I do not allow that kind of abuse of my customers, even if they have monthly pensions itself.' He nodded round and we nodded.

'Mister Moo,' said I, that being short for his name, 'sure I never wrote a book with a hard cover? You're the man that knows that.'

'Bedad and you never did, barring you did between the hours of half-two and half-three.'

'Oh, indeed and he did not,' said Maria Concepta from the corner; 'indeed and he did not ever go in for anythin' so forren as writin' books. Sure that boy, he can't read, never mind write.'

'I don't know whether he did or not,' says the Rasher. 'He attacked in print a friend of mine. One who is not in the common run of—ah-

ah-ha—'

'Now, now, "ha-ha" yourself,' said Maria Concepta. 'I'll give you "ha-ha!"'

'He attacked in print,' said the Rasher, impressively, 'a friend of mine, who is not in the common run of ha-ha—'

'Ha-ha is not proper abuse, sir,' said Maria Concepta.

'Ha-hackery,' said the Rasher. 'The man is a hack.'

I shivered my nostrils and whinnied.

'Well, now,' said Crippen, 'he has a look of the quinine speeshes,' and added with elegance, 'when you see under the gate.'

'My friend,' said the Rasher, 'the liar.'

'Ah, no, that's enough,' said Mister Moo.

'I meant a barrister,' said the Rasher with dignity.

'I'm sorry, decent man,' said Mister Moo, 'you meant a lawyer; sure no one would have an hour's luck attacking the likes of them fellows; no man of education would attack the like, and I can see you're an Eton man like meself.'

'Aye,' muttered Crippen, 'and a drinkin' man if you went into it.'

'That's not ayther here nor there, now,' said Mister Moo. 'I'm not waiting on the likes of you to tell me that.'

'But, all the same,' said the Rasher, who had been in Soho for some time, 'actually—that person.'

'Oh, indeed, now,' said Maria Concepta, 'there's no need for language the like of that. Going round calling people persons. And they not doing a ha'porth on you.'

'The lady's right,' said Mister Moo to the Rasher; 'there's no persons here.'

'No, indeed,' said Maria Concepta, 'we served and seen every class of people here, but no persons.'

'Nevertheless', screeched the Rasher.

'Oh, nevertheless', said Maria Concepta, reasonably.

'But very much the more,' said Crippen, sincerely.

'That hack,' said the Rasher, looking straight at me, 'attacked a friend of mine. A friend of humanity's. A real writer—not—' he shouted, defiantly, 'one whose name will be found on the flyleaf of thick volumes, but whose more delicate moods—'

'The same again, men?' asked Mister Moo.

He was waved away.

'But whose happiest sentiments may be found—'

'In the slim sheaf of verse,' murmured Crippen.

The Rasher nodded. 'How did you know, red—'

'Redolent of the faintest faery feylike feeling,' muttered Crippen.

'Genius,' said the Rasher respectfully. 'How did you know?'

'Never mind poor Brending Behing,' said Crippen, 'he doesn't know what he writes.'

'How so?' asked the Rasher.

'Sad case,' said Crippen, looking at me with commiseration. 'Only went to school half the time, when they were teaching the writing—can't read.'

Irish Press 28 January 1956

A seat on the Throne

I knew a man from Nicholas Street that sat on the Throne of England.

He was working for a painting contractor at the time, and must have occupied the royal seat six times a week at least.

'At every tea-break in the morning,' said the Drummer: 'at lunch-time, of course, we went out for beer.'

They were doing up Buckingham Palace at the time, and the tea was made in the usual way, in a billy-can stuck over a blow-lamp.

The Drummer sat up on the Throne because it was the handiest way of looking out into the yard, and keeping an eye out for an approaching foreman.

The Family were not in residence at the time, though this did not prevent unscrupulous persons—a plasterer's helper and a decadent scaffolder—from selling to elderly females in the pub nearby what purported to be bottles of Their Bathwater.

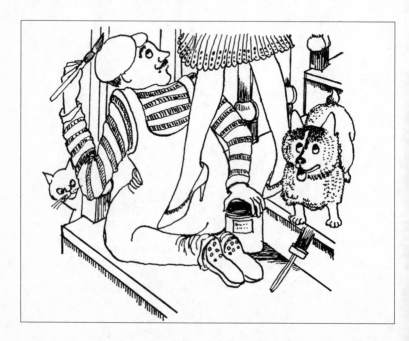

'Some of them just kept it in a bottle and looked at it,' said the Drummer, 'and there was a gentleman that bought the full of a bird-bath off them for three pints of bitter an' a pork pie. He wanted to give his budgie a dip in it for a birthday treat.'

But his finest hour was yet to come when They were returned from Their holidays. The Drummer was painting the flats and risers of a stairs leading to Their private apartments when it happened.

Her Majesty came noiselessly down the stairs and was beside him ere he knew it.

He was still bent over his work, in a kneeling position, and his head bowed devotedly as he coated the current riser.

Then a small and beautifully encased foot nudged him in the ribs, in the region of the paper-brush pocket.

In surprise he glanced up, and tried to rise, in great confusion. 'Your Majesty, I'm so sorry, I—'

But she only smiled graciously and in soothing tones remarked: 'Don't stir, Drummer. I'll step over you.'

'And when we left,' said the Drummer, 'every man got a hundred box of three greetings cigarettes.'

'There were three greetings on them?'

'There was three wrappings. Like this way. The company that made them would issue them for Christmas, and they'd have holly and ivy and Santy Clauseses and log fires and "A Happy Christmas" on the label. But then say Christmas passed, and they weren't got rid of, well, the people giving them could tear off the first label and underneath was another one, with little yellow chickens, and "A Happy Easter" on it, and if you didn't get rid of them then, you'd tear off that label and underneath was a notice saying, "They're getting stale, you'd better smoke them yourself."'

A small man drinking a fill-up for himself nodded in agreement. 'They gave us them, too, in the Palace.'

'Were you there, too?'

''Deed and I was,' said little fill-up, 'at sympathy concerts.'

'You were playing at these concerts?' I asked him.

'I don't know whether he was or not,' muttered the Drummer.

'I didn't say yet whether I was or not,' said little fill-up, 'I only said I was at the sympathy concerts. If yous want to know, I was in charge of the music mule attached to the sympathy orchestra for carrying the instruments; in particular a most unhuman big drum.'

'You weren't playing?'

'No, I had me work cut out trying to soothe the mule, and he outside nearly going mad from the noise of Beethoven's Fifth. Just as well if it had have been last, I often thought, and me struggling to keep Grace Darling—that was the mule's name on account of his being so vicious—(a joke, if yous folly me) from going wild round the Palace grounds, and we waiting to carry the instruments back. Then there was Mozart; there's a fellow come on a lot since.'

'Them was nice goings-on,' said a snarly-looking customer, 'smoking cigarettes and drinking tea on the Royal Throne of England and playing music, and the dead dying in dozens for Ireland every minute of the day. Them was nice things; oh, Mother Éire, you're rearing them yet.'

He strangled his utterance on a sob and bowed his shoulders on the counter.

'Ah, don't take it too much to heart,' said little fill-up. 'I told you, I only guided the mule.'

'Well,' said the Drummer, 'it was all aiqual to me whose ceiling I whitened. I'd wash off a stretch for the Sheikh of Arabee, once he paid the rate.'

Irish Press 18 February 1956

Snow through the window

I sat down this morning after a kipper, some mushrooms, cheese, black coffee with bread and marmalade and butter, and looked out of the window, thinking of the poor.

While the turf was blazing itself into a white heat of fragrant caressing warmth, I digested my breakfast and reflected on the excellence of my condition.

'The wicked,' I thought happily, 'prosper in a wicked world.' But, alas, not the worst of us is free from the improving influence of a good woman. My first wife came in and said, 'I thought you were doing that bit of an article today?'

I looked out the window again and shuddered.

'You're not expecting a man to work in that kind of weather?' said I, with a look at the blizzard.

But she was adamant and pointed to this masheen, as the man called it, and I only got out of the house by a mutter about a telephone call to be made from Peter's. I reflected during my hundred yards battle through the snow that if the Corporation would not build a tunnel from our house to Peter's, I'd have to get my overcoat out of pawn.

I may say that the height of good humour prevailed in this igloo of ours.

There were elderly ladies of a loyalist nature from Ballsbridge, and pensioners from the Indian Army. There were former ladies of the Sweep, two Mayo chaps off a building job on Wet Time, a deported American and a couple of African medical students, a man that sold pigs the day before yesterday, a well-known builder and a publican, equally well known in his own shop, myself and Packy from Scarriff. There were some English people over for a holiday in Peter's and a man who used to stop greyhounds for a living.

Now, it is not to be thought that we were not thinking of those less fortunate than ourselves that were stuck out in it. Nor is it to be implied that we thought lightly of the sufferings of any worker in bad weather, from the docker trying to graft over the freezing water to the man chasing a ewe up the sides of Tón-le-gaoith in the County Wicklow. But it was the way we were looking out the window and counting our blessings for ourselves.

And, as is the case in times of general dislocation, there was, as I said, the height of good humour, like what Raftery described at Galway Races:

Bhi sluagh mór daoine ann, from every airt and part,
Siad deas macánta, croidhiúl ann, and singing with a good heart,
Ag rinnce is ag órdú dighe, ag gabháil an 'Cruiscín Lán',
The day we spent in Paul's house, *maidin a' tsneachta bháin.*

That's not what Raftery wrote, but it's as well as I can remember, and go and write one of your own if you think you can do better.

I heard it told there, as the first of a series of lectures that should be entitled 'We'll neither work nor want,' the story of a man that had a slight accident in a very great industrial concern.

Your man has this accident and is laid off for a week or so, and then he comes back to be examined by the company doctor.

'But there's only one little thing,' says the doctor. 'Just a teeney weeney bit of bone. A splinter and no more, only it's aimed straight at your heart. We'll have it out in no time.'

'You will,' says your man, 'in my eye.'

'Ridiculous,' says the doctor. 'It'll only be a very slight operation, a matter of a couple of days in bed to extract this bit of bone—but,' and he calls for two minutes' silence, as these fellows will, when they're out to put someone through it, 'if you leave this little bit of bone in you it's going straight for your heart like a torpedo.'

'That little bit of bone,' says your gills, 'I make me own arrangements about, and you're not operating on me.'

The doctor sighed, and the next week your man was out on full pension, which they gave him cheerfully enough, as he wouldn't live more than a week or two to draw it, with that little bit of bone in him.

The week he got the pension he went into hospital and had the bone taken out, and last week threw snowballs at the passers-by as he waited to draw the one thousandth and eighty-sixth weekly instalment of his pension.

Something like the boneman's stroke would suit me down to the ground and keep me in out of the elements these cold days.

I was reared a pet, God love me.

Irish Press 25 February 1956

Poland is the place for fur coats

I am putting this at the top of the article, for a riddle to literary punters for the Spring Double: 'It was the best of times, it was the worst of times, you could only describe them as quare times.' Now, pick the bones out of that.

Thanks be to God, we are back to our own kind of weather. There was a sign of rain on the sky this morning and maybe we will have it before the day is out, but what call have we to be complaining? Didn't six hundred die in the continent of Europe, and a few score in England?

I know a Polish girl is married to a Dublin man, and she told me, that in her childhood, which is not long before the last war, a person facing the winter in Poland had to have a couple of fur coats.

'I suppose,' says I, 'they were dead cheap.'

'They were not,' said she, 'but about fifty pounds in your money.'

'Well, what happened, if you didn't have fifty pounds?'

'You died of the cold, and you weren't troubled by the cold thereafter.'

'I see,' says I, 'a neat arrangement for them that had fur coats.'

'Yes,' says she, 'we had great winter sports.'

'If you'd have happened to have been born a bear,' says I, 'you were in—on the first count.'

This lady told me that when she saw Ireland in her geography book, it looked so small that she thought everyone aboard went around carrying an umbrella, any time they walked round the island.

'Of course,' she said 'I know now that you are quite civilised.'

'That's shockin decent of you,' I replied, with the true courtesy of the Gael.

I was thinking along these remarks, waiting on a bus at Westland Row, last Saturday, after the Scotland-Ireland match.

There were Northern cars, with their different tax badges and their differing number plates, and ruddy, innocent young Irish faces, stuck out of the windows, shouting 'Up Ireland.'

Podgy Dubliners, like myself, waved Sinn Féin umbrellas, and like true rebels croaked, 'You, too.'

It was not that we were any more lacking in enthusiasm than our Ulster brothers for the 'combination of chemical elements called Ireland', but we were thinking of the rent, the ESB, the CIE, and anyway we live here all the time.

For all that, and secretly, it would be a mean heart never rejoiced by the greetings of these Ulster boys, for all I make jokes and sneers at the North, now and again.

Sure, when all is said and done, don't I let them make jokes about me?

Doesn't the whole of Ireland do it about the jackeens?

I was thinking, too, that there must be one unit of thirty-two counties, because I certainly could not imagine these voices raised in shouts of 'Come on Great Britain,' or 'Up the United Kingdom,' or 'Lurry them up, the Commonwealth.'

I thought back to another International match, when I spent the night in Trinity singing all manner of rebel songs, and to a Twelfth of July I spent at a party on an island in the River Seine, singing Orange songs, while the Paris river firemen played the searchlights of their boats on us, under the impression that ours was a rather premature celebration of the Quatorze Juillet.

Everyone, only the poor Irish, is allowed to have a difference between North and South.

Damn it, we can't open our mouths here but the stranger has it made into the basis for a thesis on racial relations.

In France the miner from Pas-de-Calais and the Norman farmer, even, refer to their countrymen of the South as 'les nègres', and all combine to heap the foulest abuse on Paris and its people. In Italy the Milanese and the Calabrian speak what are nearly two different languages, and in England, itself, the Geordie from Newcastle-on-Tyne speaks a dialect incomprehensible to the Cockney, who incidentally despises him as a 'Suede-basher.'

But nobody set up a Boundary Commission to separate Cannes from Caen, nor has it been suggested that there should be frontier posts from the Severn to the Wash with a Border in Birmingham, cutting the Bull Ring in Half, with the Mitre one side and the Rose and Crown the other.

And if we can't do anything more about it, the least we can do is knock Nelson off his perch.

Irish Press 3 March 1956

Up and down Spion Kop

When I was young, I used to be,
As fine a man as e'er you'd see,
And the Prince of Wales, he says to me,
'Come, join the British Army.'

Toora loora loora loo,
They're looking for monkeys in the Zoo.
And if I had a face like you,
I'd join the British Army.

Sarah Curley baked the cake;
'Twas all for poor Kate Condon's sake,
I threw meself into the lake,
Pretending I was barmy.

Toora loora loora loo,
'Twas the only thing that I could do,
To work me ticket home to you,
And leave the British Army.

On Wednesdays and I a child, there were great gatherings of British Army pensioners and pensionesses up on the corner of the North Circular, in Jimmy-the-Sports'.

When the singing got well under way, there'd be old fellows climbing up and down Spion Kop till further orders and other men getting fished out of the Battle of Jutland, and while one old fellow would be telling of how the Munsters kicked the football across the German lines at the Battle of the Somme, there'd be a keening of chorused mourners crying from under their black shawls over poor Jemser or poor Mickser that was lost at the Dardanelles.

Jimmy-the-Sports' Bar did not at all relish the British Army or anything to do with it, but a publican is of a kind above politics.

My family would be shocked out of their boots at any of us listening to such 'loyalist' carrying-on, but I—oh, woe to me in the times of Republican wrath—I lusted after false gods, and snaked in among the widows and orphans, and sat at the feet of the veterans, to sell my country for a glass of Indian ale and a packet of biscuits, and as Jembo Joyce would say, 'putting up me two hands to thank heaven that I had a country to sell'.

Indian ale is a thing like the Ballybough tram—gone out. It was sold out of a barrel in pubs and grocers' shops as well because it was a TT drink.

Us children were ardent TTs because we thought it had something to do with Stanley Woods and the Isle of Man races, and with Doctor Pat O'Callaghan, Colonel Fitzmaurice, R. N. Tisdall, John Joe Sheehy, Larry Cervi and Bertie Donnelly.

This Indian ale was like porter in appearance and it might happen at these pension days in Jimmy-the-Sports', that glasses would get mixed up and you wouldn't know what you were getting, sitting down there on the floor out of sight and snapping biscuits from one another.

Besides, the older ladies believed in a sup of porter for children of pre-Confirmation age and even said, 'Let them have a taste of it now and they'll never bother with it when they're grown up.'

Sometimes, *mo bhrón*, these theories have little or no scientific basis.

When the Imperial bounty of a grateful monarch had gone a good way in the process of liquidation, one lady was sure to stand up and sing a song about her late husband, who was a machine-gunner and met some quicker machine-gunner on the cousin's side.

My father always called it that, and said the dead or wounded of the Great War were an example to people not to be getting mixed up in family quarrels. And the Guelphs, Saxe-Gothas, Windsors, or whatever they call themselves, he regarded as the most dangerous clan in the whole of the world.

Besides, I knew the lady, and she was kind to all children, her own and any other ones, and she had a good voice, which is a thing I admire in a citizen, being no mean performer on the gargle trap myself.

Then Chuckles would stand up to give a bar. Chuckles, as far as I know, had not taken part in the European disturbances of 1914–18, nor had he played anything more than the part of a social worker in the wars of 1919–23 round the North Circular Road.

In time of siege he fed the civilian population with hams and sides of beef, augmented by flour and canned foods which he collected from the shops around. He described his collecting as 'armed begging' and only once did he meet with anything like a refusal.

At a big branch of an English combine, the manager's wife came down to say that her husband was phoning up head office in Liverpool to see what he could spare, that it was clearly contrary to the laws of God and man that people should benefit by war to the extent of eating things like ham that they never tasted in peace.

'I hope,' said Chuckles, with a pious glance at his Colt forty-five, 'your husband is in a state of grace.'

'Oh,' said the manager's wife when she saw the skit, 'I didn't know you were a milling-terry man. That's different. Will you give a receipt sir, please, with your name and rank?'

'Right,' said Chuckles, calling up his supporters.

When they'd filled the handcart, he gave his official receipt signed 'Me, Chuckles, O/C Looters', saluted and went off.

Irish Press 10 March 1956

Shake hands with an Alsatian

I wish you all a happy St Patrick's Day and that you may not go entirely short of provisions is the sincere wish of me and mine to you and yours. (You can be fairly certain that I won't—not if I have to shake paws with half the Alsatians in the country.)

Talking about Alsatians—you can knock off those brackets. I don't know what I put them up there for, only to be literary—they are not my favourite animal. I was related to an Alsatian by marriage. Wolf was his name, and he barked his head off any time I put my head in my first wife's family's door.

They always reassured me that he meant well, and that his bark was worse than his bite, but that could easy mean that his bite could be bad enough.

In any event, if he got away with a good lump of me it would not be much good running after him to get it back. He was at least a 30–50 pound dog.

I like little dogs like Pomeramanses or Petingeeses, but my favourite show animal is Anna Kelly's famous cat Groucho.

He has the longest whiskers in Catland, and I think should be more properly called Salvador Dali, after the painter, who maintains that his extra-long whiskers are the wireless aerials of his soul.

I'm not sure that my favourite animal, taken one way or another, is not Mr M. Cash's 'Unmindme' b.g. by Umidkhan, who did me a great obligement at Two-Mile-House Point-to-Point on Tuesday. But, anyway, poor old Wolf, my Alsatian-in-law, is now croaked, and *de mortuis nil nisi bom bom*, as they used to teach us in the Latin class in my old school.

The happiest animal I have seen is the greyhound Spanish Battle-ship, and I must say that he even seemed to put his connections into good humour, when all is said and done.

My grandmother had an enormous cat that went by the name of Beeshams. I can only describe it by saying that his father's name was Lynchehaun, and it looked every inch a son of its father.

It was a rather outstanding animal, by reason of the fact that it seemed to enjoy white snuff. Be damn, but that's a thing you don't often meet with in a cat, but it was the truth about Beeshams.

My granny had it rest upon her bosom, with his two front paws round her neck and his fat old head wagging from side to side with every intonation of her voice, as if he knew what she was saying.

His two eyes fixed on hers, as if she was Sir Anthony Eden and he was a licensed grocer from Bangor, Co. Down, hoping to be mentioned in the New Year's Honours List.

White snuff fell generously about her person, but Beeshams did not mind. He even sniffed the snuff, and wrinkled his chops as if he liked it.

'Me poor lanna walla,' my granny would say, under the impression that she was speaking to the beast in the Irish language.

Her ideas of that tongue were of the sketchiest, but her heart was good, and she usually addressed Beeshams in Irish for a go-off, as she maintained that only he understood her dialect.

'Me poor lanna walla,' she'd croon, and the old cat would wag his head slowly, 'sure it's the queer drisheen I'd be after begrudging you,' upon which she would produce a piece of Herr Youkstetter's good old Irish black pudding, and this happened regularly, though Beeshams was restricted to Sundays and Patrick's Day in Lent.

'Beeshams bucked,' she would moan. 'I might as well be boss in Erin if it wasn't for you, me good old bruteen.'

'What's a bruteen?' I asked her.

'A bruteen is a little cat.'

'It's no such a thing,' said I, 'being in fifth class and knowing all about *Algebair* and *Teagasc Críostaí agus an Atlantach Thuaidh agus an Tuiseal Geineamhnach Uimhir Iolraidh*, I should know.'

'You're an impudent cur to downface your own granny.'

'A little cat is "*cat beag*".'

'You caught no bug in this house barring you brought it in with you,' and she spoke into Beeshams's old face. 'Oh, culla culla, no luck.' Then she turned to me and said, 'I suppose you have the brass impertinence to tell me that "No luck" does not mean "no mice"?' and Beeshams would give a deep purr and she'd answer, 'Ah-ha, colleen bawn.'

'And if it goes to that, it should be *buachaill ban*. Beeshams is a he-cat,' I said.

'You mind your own business, me little man cut short,' she said. 'Beeshams is not asking you what he is,' and she directed her gaze into the cat's face. 'Ah, bah, carrageen?'

Irish Press 17 March 1956

My father died in war

I'm now going to give my eyewitness account of my father's death in action at the Dardanelles.

As I was saying before, I was a great attender at the celebrations of British Army pensioners and pensionesses on Wednesdays on our corner of the North Circular Road.

So this day they are all talking about a film that's on in the old Royal.

It was called *Tell England* when it was made, but they thought it more tactful to call it *Gallipoli* when it was shown here.

'Iz a mazzive pit-chewer,' said the Granny Carmody in Grenville Street language. 'Yez zee all the poo-war japs and the' coming offa the Brizidge battle chips and been mone dow-in the wawdher.'

'What Japs, granny?' I whispered up at her. 'Who were they up for in the war?'

'All the japs, the japs in the Dubal-ins—in the View-shalleers. Poor Bogo Brennan, hees ozziver was shot offa hees horse. A vunny plaze to brin' a horse, but the old quality couldn't be sebarazed-ed from their beastises. They'd even try and brin' them to bed widhem. Bogo said he lived three days on jockalate. Some said eh waz az much az ever he got at home, but all the japs waz livin on jockalate, at the Dardanelles.'

Us chisellers on the floor discussed the matter and agreed that the Dardanelles would not be a bad place to be if you got chocolate all the time as a principal article of diet, but we gathered from the conversation of the men that there were people living there called The Terrible Turks, and what they did with you, if they got their hands on you, was a matter to be whispered.

Tell England alias *Gallipoli* was a silent picture, technically speaking.

The picture got off to a good start, with the fellow in the orchestral stalls knocking hell out of his drum during the bombardment of the shore batteries.

The next thing we saw was what we were waiting for—the soldiers charging down the gang-planks of the landing craft.

From every part of the gods the screeches went up, 'Oh, there's our Mickser.' Other old ones screeched: 'Oh, take me out, I can't stick it. There's me husband in the water.'

Granny Carmody was not to be bested and let a roar out of her that you'd hear in Gallipoli, 'Oh, me own sweet onion, there he is, me poor first husband's brother.'

As the face that appeared close up that moment was that of a bearded Indian, I was very much impressed by the Granny's relations.

'Oh, there's me da.' I let out a roar for the good reason that you might as well be out of the world as out of the fashion.

'Ah, God help the poor child,' some old one screamed from behind, 'he's gone in a wakeness.' I wasn't, until she put the idea in my head and then I did and moaned, 'Da, da, da.'

The old one behind called for a nurse who was in attendance and I was brought to the manager's office and given tea and cake, while I told how I'd seen my daddy killed by one of them Turks. To tell the truth, I thought the Turks was a family, and that Turk was their name like Behan was mine.

'Don't mind the dirty little liar. Hees father was in the IRAh,' said the Granny Carmody. The next thing there was a loud crash from outside and windows smashed and plaster fell off the wall. 'That drum-player again,' said the Granny; 'he should be more careful.'

Irish Press 24 March 1956

Christmas eve in the Graveyard

A Short Story by Mick the Miller

Here published for the first time

This painting, by Tom Nisbet RHA, is called 'The Short Story'. It shows Brendan in McDaid's pub, with a pint in one hand, and a typescript in front of him. Brendan gave this typescript to the painter. The portrait was painted in 1952, and, according to a note on the back, presented to Brendan by the artist on the occasion of his marriage to Beatrice Salkeld in 1955.

The story in the typescript, called 'Christmas Eve in the Graveyard, A Short Story by Mick the Miller' is published here for the first time. Though much more sombre in hue, and rougher in language, its characters—notably Maria Concepta—and its style link it to the sequence of sketches contained in the Irish Press. *(Mick the Miller was a famous greyhound.)*

Christmas Eve in the graveyard

A Short Story by Mick the Miller

'My husband is dead this night, in that old Pigeon House, where you wouldn't put a dog if you thought anything of it. Sanitorium, how are you. Sure the same place would give you TB if you never had it. And cabbage and fish, dear Immaculate Heart of Jesus, that shed your blood for us that day, on the same plate, for Friday's dinner. And now, I'm told "Cheer up. Tomorrow is Christmas Eve." What do I care and it Christmas Eve? It'll be more like Good Friday to me. For lack of my poor husband up in Glasnevin.'

'When all is said and done,' said Denis the Bookie, 'you didn't see the bloody man in twenty years. I don't believe you'd have known him in the street, if you'd walked into him.'

'His own mother,' said Maria Concepta, 'wouldn't have known him yesterday. He was like God forgot. His poor face all fell in and two eyes staring out of his head.'

At the memory of it she bowed across to Teresa (of Avila), to give us a rossiner.

Teresa (of Avila) filled out two glasses of malt. For Denis, who, being a bookie and a man of means, never drank anything else. For her mother, Maria Concepta, who was the widow of the wake, and leaving that consideration aside, would drink whiskey out of a whore's boot, any time. She gave me another bottle of stout, as befitted my comparative youth, which was the seventeenth since leaving the pub, not counting three halves of malt I had before we shifted poor Jembo into the chapel. When we left him there for the night, till the funeral in the morning, Maria Concepta adjourned the proceedings to the boozer across from her house and ordered another bartley of drink to be sent over to us after closing time.

No matter whether she was parted from Jembo this twenty years or not, she respected him in the line of treating the people that came to his wake. His own sisters were running an opposition wake down in

[133]

Monto. But I was glad I came to Maria Concepta's, than to be down there, drinking plain porter and listening to the sisters blaming Maria Concepta for marrying Jembo in the First War, and he back from the Dardanelles.

Jembo got leave about this time and started going round with Maria Concepta. She was ten years older than him, and her husband, a sailor, lately drowned off Scotland. But I've heard said she was the finest looking woman our side of the Liffey. Red hair like a new penny, and teeth it would be a wholesome pleasure to be bit by. Jembo was a slim bit of a lad, that would be a man one minute, telling about the Turks and the war, and the men being caught on barbed wire and pulled down after their own guts into the water. The next thing Jembo would be out in the middle of the road, in his khaki, with a gang like himself, playing combo soccer with a tennis ball, and running with the other kids when a policeman would come down out of the barracks. Maybe he'd dart back into the pub and tell more about the War. How some officer got shot in the back. That was what the old women liked to hear. Granny Kearney or old Mrs O'Hare would lift their tumbler and put two eyes up to heaven from under the shawl and say:

'The blessing of Jesus Christ be on the hand that did it. May he never want, him nor his.'

They didn't mind the War so much all the same. The pubs were packed out the whole time. And once an old woman had her entrance fee, she was there for the day. Men either going from leave or coming on it. Being either welcomed or waked, as the saying had it. The women had no bigger strain on them than going to the post-office every week for the double tap on the pay-book for the ring money. Granny Kearney had three sons in it and drawing for each of them. She was never so well off, before or after. Someone read the paper in the pub one day and it said the Pope was looking for peace.

'Isn't it a civil wonder to Christ,' said the Granny Kearney, 'that the Pope, God bless him, wouldn't mind his own bloody business? Has he got three big gougers of sons that never done a tap of work in their lives, only soccer football, and introducing Fagan to young girls they were never married to? Does he want them back to persecute the heart out of us? Lying up in bed all day, smoking Woodbines. Jesus, it's enough to make you turn Protestant, the rest of your life.'

Jembo married Maria Concepta, the last day of his leave, and on the wedding night his mother and sisters came up and roared in at Maria Concepta that she was a baby-snatcher. The old woman said she was a grabber into the bargain, to do an old woman out of her separation allowance, not satisfied with what she got for her first husband, drowned in the Merchant Navy.

Jembo came out, in his Army shirt and his boy's smooth legs pink to the thighs, as he stood cold on the stairs, his bayonet in one hand and a whiskey bottle in the other.

'By the Sacramental Jesus,' he said, 'if yous don't shift out of that, I'll stick this bayonet in your shop-front.'

Any boy, to let his own mother and sisters see him without his trousers, would be capable of anything, so they went off with themselves, and the next day, the old woman went down to North Anne Street chapel and put the widow's curse on Maria Concepta.

Whether that was the cause of it or not, herself and Jembo only lived together for a couple of years. Until just after Teresa (of Avila) was born. They had a son called Seamus, killed at Normandy in the war, gone out. And another daughter, died young, called Margaret Cartena. Denis the Bookie wanted to know what better luck they expected, and the child named for the patron saint of lock hospitals.

After that, Maria Concepta didn't see Jembo for twenty years, and the last we heard of him, he was living in tally someplace. When he went into the sanatorium his fancy woman used to visit him there. Bringing him a sup of soup or that, until the nuns found out who she was. Maria Concepta told them, and his sisters told them.

'I will say for them,' said Maria Concepta, 'they put between me and poor Jembo, and I never spoke to any one of them from that good day to this, but they went like Christians to the Reverend Mother, and told her that he had only one lawful wife, and that I was her, and that this one had only been living in tally with him.

'"God bless us," said the Reverend Mother, "she must be put out of

[135]

here at once. She's getting between him and heaven. He can't die with her there.'"

'It's a well known thing, and a very well known thing,' said Teresa (of Avila), 'that a person can't die with something like that, a big sin, going on.'

'"Pitch her out at once," said the priest, "and leave her not show herself near him in life, when the soul is leaving him, that she nearly shouldered into hell-fire, or near the poor body that she was an instrument of pleasure and an occasion of sin to."'

'They got her up,' said Teresa (of Avila), 'two Sisters of Mercy, Sister Carmel of the Divine Child and Sister Agnes the Lamb, and dragged her out, she screeching in a ward full of dying people, and she trying to hold on to his hand as if she wanted to drag him after her. You'd think she would have had more shame. Then she tried to snake into the dead-house after us before they coffined him. One of my aunts chased her.'

'Oh, give her her due, she did,' said Maria Concepta.

'And,' said Teresa (of Avila), happy to hear for the first time in her life, one side of her family speaking well of the other side, 'My other aunt went after her in to the grounds, and shouted at her that if she showed herself next or near the cemetery in the morning that she'd be dug out of her.'

'I wouldn't be surprised if she chanced it,' said Maria Concepta, 'those ones do have enough of cheek to do a parish for a week.'

All the way up from the Pigeon House, and up the North Circular Road, where we all lived, years ago and happy, in spite of an odd row, for fighting is better than loneliness, over the Cross Guns Bridge and past Mountjoy Prison, I watched out for her. I had never seen her, but I thought I should know her, if she came. A car might sweep in to the cortège, and a figure heavily veiled in rich mourning, in the far corner of it. Or, at the last minute, a wreath of roses, white and red, in purple silk would be laid on the coffin, by a gloved hand from the candlelight.

I looked all round the chapel, but there was no sign of anybody except Jembo's sisters, Maria Concepta, Teresa (of Avila), Denis the Bookie and myself.

On the way up to the grave Maria Concepta began to cry, walking behind the coffin cart.

'The last time I was up here, was with poor little Margaret Cartena. It was a year after we parted and I thought the death of our little child might bring us together again. After the last of the heap of clay was put on top of her, I threw myself on it, thinking he might pick me up, "Oh, Margaret, Margaret," I cried, "My lovely darling." I thought he might hear me, and lift me up and hold me, but sure when I looked around from under my arm, I might as well be crying there yet. For where was he? Behind a tree, making his water.'

Jembo was planted and the prayers finished.

Teresa (of Avila) turned to Maria Concepta and she said:

'Look at her, Ma.'

'Where?' asked Maria Concepta.

I looked to where she pointed, but could see no one.

'The bloody bitch,' said Jembo's sister, who had been drinking the whole night through.

'Where?' I whispered to Maria Concepta.

'Ah, can't you see her there. Over be the big headstone.'

Crouched up against a tomb was a poor woman, battered shapeless by hardship, and dressed in old clothes with no meaning but covering and warmth, given her by some lady she would be doing a day's work for.

'But she looks a real poor looking old one,' I said.

'And what way would you expect her to look' said Maria Concepta, 'and she out scrubbing halls these years for me dear departed.'

When she saw us moving from the graveside, she went off down the path.

In the public house, when Maria Concepta and Teresa (of Avila) were gone to relieve themselves, Denis the Bookie said to me, in his severe and educated tones, which meant he was in humour of buying plenty of malt for himself and anyone that would drink with him:

'I suppose you were really there in the shape of a son-in-law of a sort. Aren't you marrying the Tommy's widow?'

I didn't like him to refer to Seamus as a Tommy. It made him somehow like Jembo his father, the withered remains of TB and misery we had just buried. Seamus was killed in Normandy and he only nineteen and married but a month. I didn't resent him when I was with his widow, it was even an added pleasure to follow the thrusting of his young ardent flesh. It was as if I was carrying on where he had left off in the strength of his new manhood. I said as much to Denis the Bookie.

'Well,' said Denis the Bookie regretfully forced to admit it at last, 'you are a dirty bastard. But it's a wonder, as you're at it, that you wouldn't marry the girl, and cease these inferior practices of carrying on with her, in sin. Still,' he remarked humanely at his glass of whiskey, 'I suppose you need the pension.'

Notes

In these articles and stories Brendan Behan plundered the rich vocabulary of words and references of the Dublin working class. He used a wide range of references to authors (mostly in the Irish canon such as Joyce, Yeats, Wilde, Mangan etc.); he also expected his readers to be familiar with a considerable amount of history (and, since he was writing in the *Irish Press*, from a republican point of view). As the pieces were written for a newspaper column, political and social references to the events of the day abound. These notes provide some background to the references, and explain some of the Dublin slang. Brendan was a fluent Irish speaker, and he frequently used Irish words and phrases—these are translated in the notes. Items that are repeated are explained under their first occurrence only.

The following authorities have been found particularly helpful in compiling the notes:

Brian Behan *Mother of all the Behans* London: Hutchinson 1984

Henry Boylan *Dictionary of Irish Biography* Dublin: Gill and Macmillan 2nd edition 1988

Patricia Boylan *All Cultivated People: A History of the United Arts Club* Gerrards Cross: Colin Smythe 1988

Tony Farmar: *Ordinary Lives* Dublin: A. & A. Farmar paperback edition 1995

D. J. Hickey and J. E. Doherty *A Dictionary of Irish History 1800–1980* Dublin: Gill and Macmillan paperback edition 1987

Bernard Share *Slanguage* Dublin: Gill and Macmillan 1997

Page

1   'As Joyce says': James Joyce

1   'Seán Ó Faoláin' (1900–91): writer of short stories and novels and editor of the literary magazine *The Bell* (1940–46) where he published Brendan's short story 'I Become a Borstal Boy', later developed as the autobiographical *Borstal Boy* (1958) in June 1942

1   'Brian Merriman had it weighed up . . . in "The Midnight Court"': *'Cúirt an Mhéan-Oíche'* 'The Midnight Court' by Brian Merriman (*c.*1740–1805) published in 1780, is a bawdy lament by women for the waning sexual powers of men. Whilst Brendan was in Mountjoy prison, he translated some of this poem into English.

1   'I am one of the compulsory Irish': after the founding of the Irish Free State in 1922 Irish was made a compulsory subject in State examinations, and a requirement for State employment. Brendan learned Irish from native speakers imprisoned with him in Mountjoy, Arbour Hill and the Curragh.

1   'second official language': Article 8 of the 1937 Constitution stipulates: '8.1. The Irish language as the national language is the first official language. 8.2 The English language is recognised as a second, official language.'

1   'the new breathing spaces of the Dublin people—Cabra, Crumlin, Kimmage and Ballyfermot': the Behan family moved from the friendly squalor of the Russell Street tenements in the centre of the city to a desolate new estate in Crumlin (then on the south-east outskirts of the city) in 1937. Kimmage and Ballyfermot are also in south Dublin, Cabra is on the north side.

1   'rejoicing . . . in the Christian name of "Lauri"': Cardinal Lorenzo Lauri was the Papal Legate to Ireland who presided over 'the year of the congress' (*see* below).

1   'the year of the Congress': to celebrate the 1,500th anniversary of St Patrick's arrival in Ireland, the 1932 Eucharistic Congress was held in Dublin. Nine cardinals, over a hundred bishops and thousands of priests and laypeople from all over the world attended—ten ocean liners were moored in Dublin Bay. The long sequence of devotions turned Dublin into an open-air church for a week; the discipline of the tens of thousands of people, and the precision of the organisations was said to have greatly impressed Hitler.

2   'people she didn't like by the name of Murphy': probably a reference to William Martin Murphy (1844–1919) leader of the employers' side during the 1913 labour agitation, and Larkin's bête noir.

2   'Larkin for a monicker': Larkin for a name. James Larkin (1876–1947) was a labour leader and agitator, founder of the Irish Transport and General Workers Union in 1909. He was instrumental in the labour unrest in Dublin in 1913.

2   'the great O'Toole': St Laurence O'Toole was archbishop of Dublin *c*.1170.

2   'I took part in the election': the 1932 General Election brought the Fianna Fáil party to power for the first time. Brendan was nine years old at the time.

2   'NCR': North Circular Road, the northern half of the oval ring road enclosing central Dublin, planned and built in the late 18th century

2   'the Custom House . . . had gone ablaze again': the Dublin Custom House, which contained many taxation and local government records, was attacked and fired by the IRA on 25 May, 1921 with the object of hindering British ability to govern the country.

4   'de Valera's autograph': Éamon de Valera (1882–1975): rebel leader during the Easter Rising; political leader of the anti-Treaty side during the Civil War; founded Fianna Fáil in 1926; Taoiseach and Minister for External Affairs 1932–48, Taoiseach 1951–4, 1957–59; President of Ireland 1959–73

5   'if Roger Bannister could manage the mile in four minutes': Three weeks before this article was published Roger Bannister became the first athlete to run a mile in less than four minutes (May 1954).

6   'Foxrock': a wealthy Dublin suburb.

6   'moseying': going without hurrying

6   'I could do with a rossiner myself': a stiff drink

6   'from the time of the Invincibles': the Invincibles were a republican terrorist organisation responsible for the assassinations on 6 May, 1882, of the Chief Secretary to Ireland and his Under Secretary in the Phoenix Park, Dublin. The murderers were executed and the organisation disappeared soon after.

6   'go-car of fish, fruit or vegetables': push-chair (buggy) for wheeling small children, used by street traders for transporting their wares; small wheeled cart

6   'three cross-doubles': a bet on four horses giving three doubles; usually included in the bet are six trebles and an accumulator (*see also* the note for page 27)

7   'National and Trinity and all to that effect . . . Natural Trimity College': At this period there were two university colleges in Dublin—University College, Dublin, one of the constituent colleges of the explicitly Catholic National University of Ireland and Trinity College Dublin (the only college of the University of Dublin) which was traditionally Protestant.

7   'he's on the Third Programme now . . . he could be on the First if he only minded himself': a friend of Brendan's, H. A. L. Craig, wrote poetic features for the self-consciously intellectual Third Programme (now BBC Radio 3). The First Programme was devoted to light music and quizzes.

7   'Hammongd Laying Fouingdry', 'Hammond Lane Foundry': a Dublin foundry

8   'as far as Candem Street': Camden Street, on the south side of the Liffey, where fruit and vegetables are sold from barrows and stalls

8   'Renningtom': Remington is a brand of portable typewriter.

9   'Jack *versus* Saorstát Éireann': Jack *versus* the Irish Free State. The Free State was established in 1922. The new Constitution of 1937 substituted the name Éire for Saorstát Éireann and Ireland for the Irish Free State. Since 1949 the state has been known as the Republic of Ireland. The State is the prosecutor in criminal cases.

9   'being put off the Labour': no longer allowed to collect unemployment payment from the Labour Exchange

10   'Tan war': the Black and Tans were a special military force sent to Ireland to assist the RIC (Royal Irish Constabulary) in the War of Independence, largely made up of ex-soldiers psychologically damaged by trench warfare. They carried out their activities with ruthless relish. Because of their khaki uniforms and dark

green caps and belts they were nicknamed 'Black and Tans' after a well-known Limerick fox-hunting pack.

10   'getting a few makes': a few ha'pennies (pre-decimal currency)

10   'we hadn't enough readies': enough ready cash

11   'we saw the rozzers': police

11   'TDs and would-be TDs': a Teachta Dála is a deputy to the Dáil, a member of the Irish parliament.

11   'the "Joy"': Mountjoy Prison, Dublin. Brendan served four years in Mountjoy Prison from April 1942. Because he had shot at a policeman during an Easter Rising celebration, he was categorised as a political prisoner. His experiences in Mountjoy, in particular the execution of Bernard Kirwan for murder, would become the basis for his play, *The Quare Fellow*. Whilst Brendan was in Mountjoy, he began to turn towards more cultural, literary nationalism.

11   'ganger': foreman

12   'Princess Margaret' (1930–): the sister of Queen Elizabeth; she was in the news during the 1950s because she had just broken off her romance with Group-Captain Peter Townsend, a divorcee.

13   'Boer War': from October 1899 to May 1902 Boer nationalists fought Great Britain for control of South Africa. Many Irishmen fought for the British and a monumental arch in their honour was erected at the entrance to St Stephen's Green in 1907. Two Irish brigades, led by John MacBride (later executed for his part in the Rising) and Arthur Lynch, went to fight for the Boers. Presumably because of the events of 1916–21, the Boer War looms much larger in these stories, and in Irish folk memory generally, than the First World War, in which many more Irishmen fought and died.

13   'dotey little face' (from 'dote') lovable, appealing

13   'from the crubeen to the tip of the left ear': *crúibín*: boiled pig's foot

14   'the 1906 Exhibishing': the Irish International Exhibition in Ballsbridge, Dublin, actually took place from May to November, 1907. One of the most popular attractions was a 'Somali village' in which a group of native Somalis went about their daily lives in as near a replica of home as the damps of Dublin would allow. 400,000 people visited the village during the Exhibition.

14   'His father was a chef in O'Keefe's, the knackers': buyer of worn-out horses for slaughter; every part of the animal was used, including the hooves, which were boiled down for glue.

14   'like a mishing' *see also* page 128 'it was better than a Mission': mission conducted in a parish church by a visting priest to reactivate the faith of parishioners, usually by scaring them into a vigorous fear of Hell. Joyce describes such a preacher in *A Portrait of the Artist as a Young Man*.

14   'ould Tom Moore': Thomas Moore (1779–1852) is best remembered for his *Irish Melodies*, which were published between 1807 and 1834.

14   'the wall of the cabbage factory': in East Arran Street there was a covered market and a number of fruit and vegetable merchants.

16   'you haven't a snap?': a photograph

16   'Provoke-Sergeant': Provost Sergeant, a member of the military police

16   'the Curragh races': the Curragh is the largest unenclosed area in Ireland (5,000 acres) on which are both the Curragh racecourse and the Curragh military camp.

16   'a few Tommies': British soldiers

17   'I took twenty-two bar off them': twenty-two shillings

17   'Evelyn Waugh': (male) English Catholic novelist (1903–66) whose most recent work at that time was *A Handful of Dust* (1954)

17   'Is it coddin me y'are, or what?': joking, mocking

18   '*Ná bac leis*': Don't mind him, ignore him.

20   'the time of the Economic War': a 'war' fought with tariff barriers and customs impositions rather than weapons. In June 1932 the new Fianna Fáil government stopped the payment of land annuities agreed in 1925. Britain, Ireland's main market, retaliated by taxing Irish imports, especially cattle. Ireland responded by putting duties on British goods, such as coal, white bread, jam and thousands of other goods. This caused widespread distress, especially among farmers and poor city-dwellers. The Anglo-Irish Agreement of 1938 put an end to the war.

24   'poor ould Pram . . . We called him . . . after the dog that belonged to Fill Mac Coon': the mythical Irish hero, Fionn Mac Cumhaill, had a dog called 'Bran'.

24   'Belloc says': Hilaire Belloc, an English Catholic writer (1870–1953)

24   'it's a punishable offence to put them into areas': an area is an enclosed outdoor basement space in front of a house

25   'Seán Russell' (1893–1940): took part in the Rising and became Chief of Staff of the IRA from 1938 to 1939. It was under his leadership that the IRA began its bombing campaign in Britain.

25   'he was considered a chaw of some dimensions.': tough individual (often in the form 'hard chaw')

26   'not a visit to your uncle, so early in the morning?': the pawnbroker

26   '*Balladmakers' Saturday Night*': a Radio Éireann programme in the early 1950s for which Brendan wrote scripts and sang ballads

27   'accumulators': a bet on more than three horses, dependent on all winning,

in which the odds accumulate

28   'it's only the new stuff they have in the schools. Dots and dashes.': the script then in use for the Irish language used accents and stops over letters as aspirations.

28   *'On the bright Cruiskeeen Lawn': cruiscín lán*: literally, a small, full jug; a bumper of whiskey; a well-known song; the name under which Myles na Gopaleen's famous humorous column ran in the *Irish Times* from 1941

29   *'Musha and allana, astore, tiggin too'*: the stock phrases of stage Irishry; they mean 'Well, child, love, do you understand?'

31   'see the more learned literary page of this journal': the *Irish Press* was founded in 1931. It was the official organ of de Valera's Fianna Fáil party. In the 1950s it was edited by Jim McGuinness, who had, like Brendan, taken part in the IRA's 1939 bombing campaign. He paid Brendan £5 for each article. The *Irish Press* has now ceased publication.

31   'Try MacManus, Kiely or Williams.': M. J. MacManus (1888–1951), was literary editor of the *Irish Press* from 1931 to 1951 and was followed in the post by Benedict Kiely (1919–) novelist and broadcaster. The Williams referred to may have been Desmond Williams, the historian.

31   'I pass on Cecil Ffrench Salkeld's definition [of existentialism]': Cecil Ffrench Salkeld was a painter and bohemian and the original of Flann O'Brien's Philosopher in *At Swim-Two-Birds*. He was the father of Beatrice Salkeld, Brendan's wife.

32   'the Fintan Lalor pipe band': James Fintan Lalor (1807–49) was an agrarian and nationalist agitator. He contributed to the Young Ireland newspaper, *The Nation* and took part in the Young Ireland rising in 1848.

32   'Brian Boru': the King of Ireland who defeated the Danes and their Leinster allies in the Battle of Clontarf 1014; *also* the name of a pub near Glasnevin cemetery frequently used by mourners after a funeral.

34   'An Óige': Irish Youth Hostel Association, set up in May, 1931

34   'my mother had cooked a meal for W. B. Yeats in Madam MacBride's house': William Butler Yeats (pronounced Yates, not Yeets) (1865–1939) cherished a largely unrequited love for Maud Gonne (1865–1953) who married Major John MacBride, who was executed for his part in the Easter Rising.

39   'No diving in "to put yourself out of pain" as we used to say in Dollymount': a sandy beach in north Dublin, washed by the cold Irish Sea

41   'the Martyr of the Pillar': the pillar erected in memory of Horatio Nelson (1758–1805) dominated O'Connell Street, Dublin until it was destroyed by a bomb on 8 March, 1966.

42   'an elderly gentleman inquired of the conductor whether the tram went to "Kingstown"': the Dublin township of Dún Laoghaire was renamed Kingstown in

1824 to commemorate the visit of George IV. Although the name officially re-
verted in the 1920s, it was a favourite affectation of the Anglo-Irish to continue to
refer to Kingstown.

43   'D'you think I done fifteen years in Maryboro for nothing?': Maryboro
prison, in the former Queen's County, is now Portlaoise prison, in County Laois.

44   'when the teacher . . . asked me where where our food came from I replied
"Summerhill"': Summerhill is near Russell Street in the heart of Dublin.

44   'I had heard older people speaking of Dan Breen and Tom Barry': Dan
Breen (1894–1969) and Tom Barry (1897–1980) were IRA guerilla leaders during
the War of Independence (1919–21). Breen's memoirs, *My Fight for Irish Freedom*,
suggest that he probably could have beaten the British single-handed, if he had
been allowed. Barry also wrote memoirs—*Guerrilla Days in Ireland*. Both books
are still in print.

45   'Seán Treacy' (1895–1920): a republican soldier, killed during the War of
Independence

45   'the Civil War' (1922–3): the terms of the Treaty that ended hostilities
with Britain in 1921 were unacceptable to many of those who fought the War of
Independence. Deputies who opposed the Treaty were defeated in the Dáil vote on
the issue and walked out in protest. During the course of the Civil War that en-
sued, atrocities were committed on both sides. Most famously, the Provisional Government executed seventy-seven irregular (republican) prisoners over a five-month
period. On 24 May, 1923, Éamon de Valera called on the irregulars to end the
fighting and dump their weapons. Although no more than 700 people died, the
Civil War left scars that took generations to heal.

45   'Poor Henrietta caught a bad cold at Parnell's funeral': Charles Stewart
Parnell (1846–91), political leader for land reform and home rule was leader of the
Irish Parliamentary Party at Westminster from 1880 to 1890. His popularity and
influence were so great that he became known as the 'uncrowned king of Ireland'.
His funeral procession to Glasnevin took place in Dublin on 11 October 1891, and
was the occasion of a mass outpouring of emotion unequalled until Michael Collins'
funeral procession (also to Glasnevin) in 1922. Brendan's funeral procession to the
same graveyard in 1964 was described as 'the biggest since Collins'.

46   'fit for the puzzle factory': asylum for the insane

46   'It was the Gorman yesterday': St Brendan's Hospital, Grangegorman (now
closed) was a mental hospital.

49   'in place of Wolfe Tone's monument': Theobald Wolfe Tone (1763–98) was
one of the leaders of the United Irishmen who wanted to unite Catholics, Protestants and Dissenters in the struggle against the British. After the failed attempt to
invade Ireland with a French fleet he was captured, and committed suicide in prison.

49 'my accent is as much of a brogue as Barry Fitzgerald's': Fitzgerald (1888–1961) was a stage and film actor acclaimed in America for his roles in Seán O'Casey's *Juno and the Paycock* and *The Plough and the Stars*. He worked in Hollywood for twenty years, winning an Oscar and appearing in John Ford's *The Quiet Man*.

49 'the Six Counties': a way of referring to Northern Ireland; the Government of Ireland Act 1920 put in place the state of Northern Ireland, which comprises six of the nine counties of Ulster.

49 'Fenians or Orangemen': terms used, often pejoratively, to refer to Catholics and Protestants in Northern Ireland. After the abortive rising in 1867, 'Fenian', used abusively or sympathetically depending on the speaker's viewpoint, became a general term for the physical force wing of Irish nationalism. The Orange Order, a sort of Masonic Lodge for Ulster Protestants, was founded in 1795. Its marches on the Twelfth of July now act as the focus of grass-roots opposition to a united Ireland.

50 'famous for its murders': the multiple murderer John Christie was hanged in 1954. The fact that Timothy Evans had been hanged some years before for one of his murders sparked a vigorous debate on capital punishment, a theme Brendan explored in *The Quare Fellow*. Neville Heath was convicted of the brutal murder of a woman in a London hotel in 1946. John Haigh, the 'acid-bath murderer', was hanged for killing six women and disposing of their bodies in baths of industrial acid.

51 'the foreign games controversy': the GAA (Gaelic Athletic Association) forbade its members to play or even watch certain games identified as non-Gaelic or foreign.

51 'Croker': Croke Park, Dublin, the headquarters and main playing ground of the GAA

52 'the attempt to rescue Frank Carty': Frank Carty (1899–1972) was Editor of the *Irish Press* 1957–62. He fought in the South Wexford Brigade during the War of Independence and on the anti-Treaty side during the Civil War.

52 'Teddy Boys': more or less violent gangs of youths instantly recognised by their long 'Edwardian' frock coats, deep crèpe-soled shoes and 'duck-arse' haircuts

53 'I could see the headstone in the Nevin': Glasnevin Cemetery in Dublin where Daniel O'Connell, Charles Stewart Parnell, Michael Collins and Brendan are all buried. Brendan's last play, *Richard's Cork Leg*, is set in this cemetery. On 5 April 1942, he took part in an Easter Rising commemoration in Glasnevin. During a skirmish between republicans and the police, he shot at a detective. He was sentenced to fourteen years in prison but was released four years later under a general amnesty.

53 '*Breandáin Ó Beacháin, coshálta chun báis ar Dhroichead Waterloo, 1954.*': Brendan Behan, kicked to death on Waterloo Bridge, 1954.

54   'painter's apprentice': Behan began learning his trade as a housepainter at Bolton Street Technical School, Dublin in September 1937. From November 1946 to April 1954, painting was his main source of income. Union rates at the time were 4s an hour for a 44 hour week, or just over £9 a week.

54   'running out for the charge-hand's curer': a drink to cure a hangover, a hair of the dog that bit you

54   'the day Workman won the National': the Grand National steeplechase held every year in Aintree, Liverpool, is one of the highlights of the British racing calendar. Because of the large fields and tough fences, the National was a notoriously difficult race to predict.

54   'to force the attentions of Messrs John Ryan and Frederick May': John Ryan (1925–92) was the editor of the literary magazine *Envoy* (1943–51). His memoir of 1950s literary Dublin *Remembering How We Stood* was published in 1975. Frederick May (1911–85) was Music Director of the Abbey for fifteen years; in 1948 he founded the Music Association of Ireland. He harboured an unrequited passion for Brendan.

55   'in company with another military refugee from the trade, Mr Joseph Tomelty': Joseph Tomelty (1911–95) was a housepainter, playwright, novelist and actor. He wrote and starred in a very popular BBC radio soap.

56   'the Lane Pictures': Hugh Lane (1875–1915) donated 39 pictures to the Dublin Municipal Gallery, on condition that a new building be built for them. Dublin Corporation rejected the idea, so he bequeathed the pictures to the National Gallery in London. He died in the sinking of the *Lusitania* in 1915, leaving an unwitnessed codicil to his will reversing this decision. Despite this, the British retained the pictures, which many took as a typical piece of legalistic bullying on the part of the former colonial power. '

56   'Countess Markievicz' (née Constance Gore-Booth) (1868–1927): of Anglo-Irish background, she took part in the Rising and was sentenced to death but was spared because of her sex. She became the first woman member of the London parliament, but, like all Sinn Féin MPs, refused to take her seat. She was Minister for Labour in the First Dáil, and was an active opponent of the Treaty. In 1927, she became a Fianna Fáil TD.

56   'Thomas Bodkin' (1887–1961): Director of the National Gallery from 1927 to 1935

56   'Oliver St John Gogarty' (1878–1957): surgeon, poet and writer on whom Buck Mulligan in *Ulysses* is based. His long and snobbish memoirs *As I Was Going Down Sackville Street* were published in 1936.

56   'Lady Gregory' (1852–1932): patron of W. B. Yeats, and co-founder of the Abbey Theatre

56   'Seán O'Casey' (1880–1964): playwright of the Dublin slums. His best-known plays are *The Shadow of a Gunman* (1923), *Juno and the Paycock* (1924) and *The Plough and the Stars* (1926).

56   'Sarah Purser' (1848–1943): artist and patron. Her fine portrait of Brendan's mother, Kathleen, now hangs in the National Gallery in Dublin

56   'the late Mr William Martin Murphy' (1844–1919): leader of the employers' side during the 1913 labour agitation and lock-out

57   'in a letter to his own *Irish Independent*': the national daily newspaper founded in 1891 was bought by William Martin Murphy in 1905. It became the unofficial voice of conservative, Catholic Ireland.

58   *'came meal a vault yeh': céad míle fáilte*: a hundred thousand welcomes

58   'over the stage in the Queen's': the Queen's Theatre, Pearse Street, housed the Abbey from 1951 after it was gutted by fire, until the new theatre was opened in 1966. None of Brendan's work was performed by the Abbey until 1967.

58   'Lester Pigott let him down': the well-known British jockey won his first Epsom Derby in 1954 at the age of eighteen.

59   'the butt-end of Moore Street': city-centre street market presided over by generations of formidable Dublin matriarchs

59   'Me-Hall!': *Micheál*: Michael

59   'a bottle of Johnny-jump up': potent brand of cider

60   'and you will sleep in peace until I come for thee': the last line of 'Danny Boy', a famous ballad

62   'getting it up for me': trying to annoy me

63   'what happened your gills?': your man

63   'your friend in the CIE': Córas Iompair Éireann: the national transport service set up on 8 December, 1944

64   *'Dublin Opinion'* (1922–72): a humorous monthly magazine which presented a largely inoffensive, Dublin-centred, middle-class point of view

64   'this *teóranta* or that *teóranta*': limited, as in limited company

64   'this kind of Coombe-olatry': the Coombe is a working-class area of Dublin, south of the Liffey, near St Patrick's Cathedral.

64   'my native Monto': red light district to the east of O'Connell Street (and somewhat south of Russell Street) cleared of its brothels by moral activists in the early 1920s, following the departure of the British army

65   'Joe Lynch': star of a popular comedy programme on Radio Éireann called *Living with Lynch*

66   'like a Curse Umpar Errin tour of the country': Córas Iompair Éireann (CIE)

67 'a poem . . . be Mangle, James Claryawance Mangle': James Clarence Mangan (1803–49) nationalist poet. His most famous poem is 'My Dark Rosaleen'.

68 'Sinn Féin': a political movement for Irish independence developed between 1905 and 1908 and reorganised after the Rising (with which it had nothing to do) by de Valera who became its president in 1917. Sinn Féin won a decisive victory in the 1918 general election but its MPs refused to take their seats at Wesminster. The Treaty of 1921 split Sinn Féin; pro-Treatyites formed Cumann na nGaedheal (subsequently merged into Fine Gael). De Valera left Sinn Féin and founded Fianna Fáil in 1927.

68 'one-and-one': fish and chips, a portion of each

68 'Mitchelstown': on 9 September, 1887, the police opened fire on a crowd attending a Land League meeting, killing three people. The incident became known as 'the Mitchelstown Massacre'.

70 'Roto': a cinema attached to the Rotunda Maternity Hospital

70 'a bit of gas': a bit of fun

70 'he rescued Lady Smith': Ladysmith, a town in South Africa, was beseiged by the Boers in 1900 and, after well-organised resistance, relieved by the British Army. The town was named after the wife of Sir Harry Smith, a Waterloo veteran, who was Governor of the Cape 1847–52.

7 1 'too sick to wait for the market': the pubs opened early in the fruit and vegetable market.

71 'Hanna Bow Lane': Anne Boleyn, one of the beheaded wives of Henry the Eighth

72 'sleeveen': sly, ingratiating person

73 'before you could say Lennox Robinson': playwright and manager of the Abbey Theatre, Robinson (1886–1958) wrote limp pieces of literary chat for the *Irish Press* which appeared on the same page as Brendan's column.

73 'assmacrockery': aristocracy

73 'looking like the late Rin-tin-tin going to do something faithful': a dog star of Hollywood films much given to heroic and unlikely rescues

73 *'Oh, go raibh maith agat go deo, a ghrá, mar gheall ar an bhfáilte lách sin.'* 'Oh, thank you for ever, my love, for that warm welcome.'

74 'somewhere between Ameyens and Paris': Amiens Street railway station, Dublin (now Connolly station), pronounced Ameyens

75 'old George Roberts' had been managing director of Maunsell, the Dublin publishers of George Bernard Shaw, Yeats, George Moore and Joyce. Although technically accomplished and with an enviable list of authors, Roberts had no business sense, and the firm went into liquidation in the 1920s.

75   'Pearse's oration over the grave of Rossa': the funeral in Glasnevin of Jeremiah O'Donovan Rossa (1831–1915) , a founding member of the Fenians, gave Padraig Pearse (1879–1916) the opportunity for a famously stirring oration. Pearse was responsible for the central rhetoric of the Easter Rising. He was executed on 3 May, 1916.

75   'the Rising': originally intended as the focus of a national uprising, the Easter Rising of April 1916 disrupted the centre of Dublin, but failed militarily. 1,357 people (more than half of whom were non-combatants) were killed or severely wounded. After the execution of the leaders, the Rising became the symbol of the nationalist struggle for independence.

75   'I was giving Tom Ashe and Dick Mulcahy a hand': Thomas Ashe (1885–1917), who died on hunger strike, led the Irish Volunteers at the Battle of Ashbourne, County Meath during the 1916 Rising. Richard Mulcahy (1886–1971, leader of Fine Gael 1944–59) was second-in-command.

76   'the writer Valentin Iremonger' (1918–91): poet and diplomat, poetry editor of John Ryan's influential journal *Envoy*

76   'I was in the Fianna': named after the mythical band of followers of Fionn MacCumhaill, Fianna Éireann was the youth wing of the republican movement set up by Countess Markievicz and Bulmer Hobson in August 1909. Brendan joined this organisation in April 1931.

76   'Tom Clarke's gleeful remark': an old Fenian, Thomas Clarke was the oldest of the executed leaders of the Easter Rising.

76   'written by my Uncle Peadar': Peadar Kearney (1883–1942) was Brendan's uncle and author of 'The Soldier's Song', which became the Irish national anthem. He fought in Jacobs' factory during the Easter Rising, and was interned during the War of Independence.

77   '*Erin go bragh*': *Éire go brá*: Ireland forever

77   '*stuck in his craw*': throat

77   '*Here's to Pearse and Connolly and Plunkett that died, And Tom Clarke and MacDonagh, MacDermott, MacBride, And here's to Seán Heuston . . .*' All eight men were executed for their part in the Easter Rising of 1916. The first six were signatories of the Proclamation of the Irish Republic.

78   'the Union': the Poor Law of 1838 divided the parishes of Ireland into 130 unions, each centred on a market town where a workhouse or union house was built for the relief of the poor. The system, though better than nothing, completely failed to cope with the Great Famine.

80   'capernosity': competence, flair

81   'china': cockney rhyming slang—china plate, mate

84   '*alanna machree*': *a leanbh mo chroí*: child of my heart

84   'Tailteann Games': an Irish version of the Olympics held in 1924, 1928 and 1932 to coincide with the Olympics, so that US and Austalian athletes already in Europe could take part. The Tailteann Games were described by the *Irish Independent* as 'a racial re-union of the scattered children of the Gael'. Brendan was one year old when the events described in 'The tinkers . . . ' were supposed to take place.

84   'Russell Street': a street near Mountjoy Square, where Brendan grew up

84   'DWD': Dublin Whiskey Distillery

85   'jennet': a mule

85   'rooly-booly': *ruaille buaille,* a commotion, a row

85   'John Devoy' (1842–1928) organised Fenian infiltration of the British Army in the 1860s. In 1871 he went to America where he became a prominent member of Clan na Gael. In 1924 he visited Ireland for the Tailteann Games.

86   'Angelica Kauffman's ceiling': Angelica Kauffman (1741–1807) was a Swiss-born artist famous for portraits and classical scenes. Painted ceilings by her are rare in Dublin.

86   'in the rats': suffering from delirium tremens

87   'the Great War, as it used to be called': the First World War (1914–18). By 1916 over 150,000 Irishmen, many from the Dublin tenements, were fighting in the British Army.

88   'IRA': the Irish Republican Army originated as the army of the Irish Republican Brotherhood (founded 1858) and re-emerged at the time of the Easter Rising. The IRA fought the War of Independence and after the Truce split into pro- and anti-Treaty factions. The anti-Treaty irregulars or republicans retained the title of the IRA. For the rest of the 1920s, the movement was forced underground, and was riddled with internal divisions. In April 1938, Séan Russell became chief-of-staff of the IRA, and he began making plans for an IRA campaign in Britain. In August 1939 an IRA bomb in Coventry killed five people; Peter Barnes and James MacCormack were later executed for allegedly carrying out the attack. Brendan Behan joined the IRA in 1937, and in November 1940, he was sent to Liverpool on a reconnaissance mission and was arrested soon after his arrival. By a coincidence that Brendan never forgot, he stood trial in the Liverpool Assizes on the same day that Barnes and MacCormack were executed. He was sentenced to Feltham open prison, and in March 1940, he was transferred to Hollesley Bay borstal. In December 1941, he was released and deported.

88   'Cumann na nGaedheal': political party that evolved from the pro-Treaty side in the Civil War. It was launched in March 1923, and after losing the General Election of 1932 merged with others to form Fine Gael in September 1933.

88   'chisellers': children

88   'in the cod': joking

88   'Bodenstown Sunday': republican commemoration at the grave of Wolfe Tone in Bodenstown, County Kildare

90   'Twelfth of July': on 1 July, 1691, William III defeated James II at the Battle of the Boyne; after this battle, James fled to France. On 12 July each year (a change in the calendar meant that the 1st became the 12th of July), Ulster Orangemen commemorate this victory, marching with bands and banners in many parts of the North, including County Donegal. These marches, perceived as triumphalist and anti-Catholic, have been the source of much contention.

91   *bolg in áirde*: belly up

92   'dodge into Mac's': McDaid's pub in Harry Street, a favourite poets' pub during the 1950s

92   'Humphrey O'Sullivan' (1780–1838): a schoolmaster of Callan, County Kilkenny; he developed his facility with Irish by writing a diary in that language between 1827 and 1835.

92   *'a mhic'*: my son

92   'Knock': a place of pilgrimage in County Mayo

94   'bona fide': the licensing laws allowed bona fide travellers to get a drink at any time. *Also* certain well-known pubs on the perimeter of Dublin where after-hours drinking was legal on the grounds that the clientele were bona fide travellers from the city.

94   'coddle': a dish of sausages, rashers and potatoes fried together

94   'gargle': alcoholic drink

96   'that ould Bridewell': courthouse and gaol

96   'East Finglas': a Dublin suburb

97   'St Stephen's Night . . . and I never heard it called Boxing Day': the day after Christmas—the English and the Anglo-Irish call it Boxing Day.

99   *'gan teanga, gan tír'*: without a language, without a country

100   'Could I have a Dinneen?': the Irish–English Dictionary prepared by the Rev. Patrick Dinneen (an tAthair Pádraig Ó Duinnín) in 1904 for the Irish Texts Society. It was the standard reference work for many years. Here, Dinneen is mistaken for drisheen (black pudding).

100   'a kind of Cork hoarze doovray': hors d'oeuvre

100   'the mark of the stir-about spoon': porridge associated with charity

101   'gorilla dazes in Ireland': Tom Barry's memoirs of his time in the IRA during the War of Independence, *Guerrilla Days in Ireland*, were published in 1949.

101 'Joyce is useless': Joyce's *Ulysses*

101 'not knowing the man, TG': Thank God

101 '*Garda Seo Caughtyeh*': *Garda Síochána* (Guardians of the Peace): the Irish police force which was set up in August, 1923

101 'the new Greene': Grahame Greene, an English Catholic writer, published two novels in 1955, one of which was *The Quiet American*.

102 '*an bhfuil cead agam dul amach*': 'have I permission to go outside?'—an Irish phrase early learned by generations of school children, asking for permission to go to the lavatory

104 'That's what Lord Roberts says to me in Blamevontame': in March 1900, Bloemfontein, the capital of the Orange Free State, was abandoned by the Boers and captured by the British army without a fight.

104 'Egg Wiped': Egypt. Unlike Kitchener, Roberts did not serve in Egypt.

104 'Shifty cush': shufti cush (from the Arabic); soldiers' slang for the female genitalia (P. Beale *Dictionary of Slang and Unconventional English* London: Routledge 1989)

105 'Mendecency Institution': the charitable Mendicity Institution, founded in 1818 and still active in 1997, provided daily relief to thousands, though in a highly authoritarian way.

105 'the one with the face of a DMP man': Dublin Metropolitan Police, founded in 1887, noted for their height

108 'mild and gentle like a talk about Partition on the Third Programme': the partition of the country into two states after the War of Independence and the Treaty has been the cause of much bloodshed.

111 '*Living with Lynch*': a popular Radio Eireann comedy programme starring Joe Lynch

111 Moore, George (1852–1933): Irish novelist much influenced by the fastidious French style of realism

111 'us National schoolboys': National schools are the state primary school system.

111 'between the hours of half-two and half-three': in an attempt to stop people drinking all day pubs in Dublin were closed between 2.30 and 3.30 pm—the 'holy hour'. The holy hour was abolished in 1988.

117 'ladies of the Sweep': the Irish Hospitals Sweepstake employed over 4,000 people at its height, many with republican connections.

118 '*bhí sluagh mór daoine ann, Siad deas macánta, criodhiúl ann, Ag rinnce is ag órdu dighe, ag gabháil an "Cruiscin Lán", . . . maidean a' tsneachta bháin*': There

[153]

was a large crowd there, nice, honest and hearty, dancing and ordering drinks and singing the 'Cruiskeen Lawn' . . . the morning of the white snow . . .

118   'Raftery': Antoine Ó Rafteire (*c.* 1784–1835) a blind folk-poet

120   'Spring Double': two British horse races always held in spring, the Grand National and the Lincoln.

121   'the ESB': the Electricity Supply Board

121   'jackeens': Dubliners

121   'the Boundary Commission': established in 1924 to determine the boundaries between Northern Ireland and the Irish Free State. In 1925 the boundary was fixed as it had been by the Government of Ireland Act 1920 and the Treaty of 1922.

123   'Spion Kop': a hill in South Africa taken by the British with great loss of life during the Boer War, and subsequently abandoned

123   'the Battle of Jutland' (1916): the only major encounter between the British and German fleets during the First World War

123   'keening': *ag caoineadh*, crying, grieving aloud

123   'the Dardanelles': scene of the disastrous attempt to invade Turkey in 1915, during the Great War. Many Irish soldiers, especially in the Dublin Fusiliers, died during the ensuing series of battles, particularly in Suvla Bay.

124   'Stanley Woods': Dublin motorcyclist (1903–93) who won ten TT motorcycle victories in the Isle of Man

124   'Doctor Pat O'Callaghan' (1905–91): Cork athlete who won a gold medal in the hammer at the 1923 and 1932 Olympic Games.

124   'Colonel Fitzmaurice': Dublin-born James C. Fitzmaurice (1898–1965) learned to fly in the Royal Flying Corps. He was co-pilot on the first east–west flight across the Atlantic in 1928.

124   'R. N. Tisdall': (1907–) winner of a gold medal for the 400m race in the 1932 Olympic Games

124   '*mo bhrón*': my sorrow

126   'happy St Patrick's Day': All the pubs were closed on this day, so the only place to buy alcoholic drink was at the annual Dog Show in the RDS.

127   Anna Kelly: an *Irish Press* journalist

127   'his father's name was Lynchehaun': James Lynchehaun (1858–1918), a dangerous man who viciously assaulted a woman landowner on Achill, and burned her house. After a spectacular escape from Maryboro (Portlaoise) prison to the US, British attempts to extradite him made Lynchehaun a cause célèbre among nationalists.

127 'poor *lanna walla*': poor *leanbh aillean:* poor lovely child

128 'drisheen': black pudding (made from pigs' blood and meat)

128 '*bruteen*': little brute; '*brúitín*' means mashed potatoes

128 '*Algebair* and *Teagasc Criostaí agus an Atlantach Thuaidh agus an Tuiseal Geineamhnach Uimhir Iolraidh*': Algebra, Catechism and the North Atlantic and the genitive case and plural numbers

128 'downface': to put down, to make a person lose face

128 '*colleen bawn*': *cailín bán*, white girl. *The Colleen Bawn* (1860), a play by Dion Boucicault, narrates the murder of of a young woman by two County Clare squireens.

128 '*buachaill bán*': literally 'white boy'; usually used to mean 'the whiteheaded boy', the favourite

128 'carrageen': carrageen moss is a seaweed rich in nutrients and gelatine, used in folk cures.

134 'combo soccer': football practice in the street

134 'three big gougers of sons': 'Gougers were cornerboys, gurriers, yobs, hooligans, streetwise kids . . .' (Bob Geldof)

135 'lock hospitals': the Westmoreland Lock Hospital (and other Lock hospitals in Ireland) catered for patients suffering from sexually transmitted diseases.

135 'living in tally': living 'in sin' with someone to whom you are not married. In pre-famine times the Irish mistress of a member of the landlord class was called a 'tally-woman'.